PELICAN BOOKS

A 479

RADIO ASTRONOMY

F. GRAHAM SMITH

D1464434

F. Graham Smith

RADIO ASTRONOMY

—

*Hardly do we divine the things that are on
earth, and the things that are close at hand
we find with labour, but the things that are
in the heavens, who ever yet traced out?*

WISDOM OF SOLOMON: 9, 16

PENGUIN BOOKS

Penguin Books Ltd, Harmondsworth, Middlesex

U.S.A.: Penguin Books Inc., 3300 Clipper Mill Road, Baltimore 11, Md

AUSTRALIA: Penguin Books Pty Ltd, 762 Whitehorse Road,
Mitcham, Victoria

—

First published 1960
Second edition 1962

—

Copyright © F. Graham Smith, 1960, 1962

—

Made and printed in Great Britain
by The Whitefriars Press Ltd
London and Tonbridge

—

The gravure inset printed by
Vandyck Printers Ltd.
London

*Text figures drawn by
Ronald Dickens*

Contents

Contents

List of Plates

List of Figures

Introduction

RADIO astronomy may be defined as 'the study of heavenly bodies by the reception of the radio waves which they emit'. The name is a fairly recent one, perhaps six years old, and it is unlikely that any dictionary yet carries such a definition. The subject itself is about twenty-five years old, if we date it from the first reception of radio waves from outside the earth. From a chance observation of a natural oddity, and from the more systematic but still accidental results of wartime radar research, radio physicists began to build a new science. After the war this new branch of radio physics grew closer and closer in its association with traditional astronomy, until the time when the astronomers of the Mt Palomar Observatory turned the 200-inch telescope to the position found by radio physicists for the largest source of radio waves in the sky. The result of that joint quest was of equal interest to both sciences, and the new subject began to be known as radio astronomy.

The name is a good one. Those who study the sun and the stars by their radio waves owe an enormous debt to the optical astronomers who have accumulated such a wealth of knowledge in thousands of years of scientific observation and study. If our knowledge of the universe were derived from radio astronomy alone, we should find it hard to make any sense of the radio waves we receive. But as well as providing those essentials of the science, the system of stellar coordinates, the star catalogues, and the Nautical Almanac, conventional astronomy also provides brilliant flashes of information from its history to illuminate some of the strange radio phenomena in the sky. In 1054 Chinese astronomers recorded faithfully the position and appearance of a supernova that appeared then, and this recording has made possible a true synthesis of optical and radio studies of the nebula in our galaxy known as the 'Crab'. This nebula is a powerful source of radio waves, one of the first discovered, and its association with a recorded supernova nine hundred years ago led to some detective work on other recorded supernovae. Two others have

11

been observed as faint radio stars, those recorded by Tycho Brahe in 1572 and Kepler in 1604, before the development of the telescope. It is exceptionally fortunate for so new a subject to have assistance from the tradition of patient accurate observation and recording of astronomers through the centuries. One may multiply instances of the dependence of radio astronomy on optical astronomy just as long as one may enumerate separate radio sources in the sky; the most vital dependence is in fact common to them all, that is the complete dependence of radio on optical astronomy for the measurement of distances. Without distances, the radio sources would only appear as painted on the surface of the crystal sphere of the ancient philosophers, instead of being distributed in depth throughout the whole of the observable universe.

There is a parallel between the growth of optical and radio astronomy, in the failure of both to appreciate immediately the value of their major instruments when first they appeared. From the time of Galileo's observations of Jupiter's moons and of sunspots in 1604 the scientific use of the telescope seems to have been negligible until the early nineteenth century. The sunspot cycle, for example, was not discovered until 1840, and not much idea of the shape of our galaxy was obtained until the time of Herschel. Science moves more rapidly nowadays, but from 1932 when Jansky discovered cosmic radio waves, until 1946, when wartime research provided a separate stimulus, the only radio astronomer was one lone amateur, Grote Reber. A great opportunity was lost during these years, for since then radio communications have grown so rapidly that the longer wavelengths are all but closed to radio astronomy by overwhelming man-made radio interference.

Often the strongest radio waves are found to come from the faintest visual objects in the sky, or even apparently from nowhere, while the brightest stars emit radio waves too feeble to be detected. Some of the bright radio stars have been found to be galaxies at a very great distance, and radio astronomy now appears to be providing the most powerful means of exploring the furthermost parts of the universe. Many radio astronomers believe that this new extension of the boundaries of perception will help to unravel one of the most absorbing questions of all time, the question of the origin of the universe.

This book attempts a survey of the whole of this wide subject. Inevitably it must do less than justice to parts of it, and inevitably the parts which are treated more fully are those with which the author and the radio observatory at Cambridge have been particularly concerned.

The radio universe is in many ways dissimilar to the familiar visible universe, but we can nevertheless divide it up according to a familiar pattern. We can examine the sun, the moon, and the planets, in quite separate chapters. Our own Galaxy requires several chapters, since it has a complicated structure which can be looked at in several different ways; there are therefore chapters on its overall structure, on its spiral structure, and on the patches of hot ionized hydrogen gas to be found in the arms of that spiral. Radio stars, the most unexpected features of the radio universe, occupy four chapters, partly because they comprise a very wide variety of objects, most of which are more properly to be called radio nebulae, but more particularly because they include some of the most distant objects known to astronomy. It is in this field that we make contact with cosmological problems.

In radio astronomy our advances in knowledge are immediately dependent on the development of new techniques in aerials and in receivers, the two components of a radio telescope. Some mention of radio telescopes must be made as the survey of the results and significance of radio astronomy proceeds, but most of the description and discussion of these complicated instruments is left to the last chapters of the book. Here also can be found a brief list of the principal radio observatories of the world.

CHAPTER 1

The Origins of Radio Astronomy

RADIO astronomy, a very young science, is a vigorous offshoot of a discipline whose roots are found in our earliest recorded history. Those who first observed and wondered at the courses and constellations of the stars, and the wanderings of the planets, had no instruments to extend their observation beyond the perception of keen eyes. But in 2000 B.C., in Babylon, astronomers had already established a system of time-keeping based on their observations of the sun and the stars, dividing the year into twelve months, and the day into hours, minutes, and seconds. And sailors of the same period had learned to navigate with the help of the stars.

At a time when much of life was regulated by the seasonal movements of the sun and stars, hand in hand with the practical science of astronomy grew up the unnatural one of astrology. Observers of the motions of the moon and the planets through a sky of stars, long since mapped and divided into constellations, built up an elaborate science of observation and prediction. Some of the accurate observations of eclipses have proved of great interest in modern dynamical astronomy, but it may safely be said that by far the largest part of the total of human astronomical effort has gone into the profitless direction of trying to assess character and to predict the future fortunes of individuals by the study of the positions of the sun and planets on their date of birth, conception, marriage, or other important occasion. Out of this morass of astrology emerges a rational understanding of the dynamics of the solar system, and eventually the science of astrophysics, an intriguing endeavour to understand and to explore the universe around us. There is now no science with a greater popular appeal.

The practical importance of time-keeping and navigation ensured that positional astronomy was treated as a serious study for its own sake, especially in maritime countries. Even before the invention of the telescope, the accurate observations of Tycho Brahe of Denmark enabled Kepler to formulate precise laws of motion of the planets. On the basis of these observational laws, Newton was able to show that the force of gravitation was a universal force, applying as well between the moon and the earth, and the planets and the sun, as it does between the earth and an apple. With this new concept, the notion that man held a special position at the centre of the universe vanished, and the modern inquiry into the nature of the heavens began.

We may ask how it comes about that astrophysics is such a young subject when astronomy itself is 4,000 years old. But an inquiry into the nature rather than the arrangement of the stars requires tools that extend our perception of the universe beyond simple visual observations. The first great step towards knowledge of the stars themselves came with the invention of the telescope in the time of Galileo, although nothing was known even of the distance of any star until about 120 years ago, when the first parallax measurement of distance was made. To contemplate the composition even of the members of the solar system must at that time have seemed unthinkable. Dynamical studies gave eventually the masses and average densities of the planets, but nothing could be known of their chemical composition, or of their temperatures, or indeed of physical conditions on any heavenly body. The biggest revolution in astronomy was the introduction of spectroscopy, which came like a key to unlock all mysteries.

It was again Newton who first showed that white light can be split into many colours, all of which are simultaneously present in the white light, and who explained the action of the spectroscope which is used in every observatory for this purpose. In 1802 Wollaston showed that sunlight, when split up in a prism spectroscope, produced a spectrum in which there were narrow dark lines, the lines which are named after Fraunhofer, a later discoverer of the same phenomenon. G. G. Stokes was able to explain later that the light that should have filled these gaps in the sun's spectrum had been absorbed by atoms in the corona surrounding the sun. Each separate element absorbed its own colour or wavelength, and the wavelengths peculiar to each could be determined in the laboratory by measuring the spectrum of light emitted by electric discharges in vessels containing some of each element in turn. The Fraunhofer lines thus provide nothing less than a list of the kind of atoms to be found in the sun's corona, and hence in the substance of the sun itself. Perhaps the most outstanding success of spectroscopy was the discovery by Lockyer, in 1878, of a strong Fraunhofer line in the green part of the solar spectrum at a wavelength corresponding to no known element. He suggested that it came nevertheless from an element, present in the sun but not at that time isolated on the earth, and he named it 'helium'. This gas is, of course, familiar today for its use in balloons, for many industrial uses, and as an end product of the fusion of hydrogen nuclei.

With the additional tool of spectroscopy, astronomy in the middle of the nineteenth century had acquired a new breadth in looking at the heavens. The view had changed from a peep through a narrow crack to a broad vista through the wide window of the visible spectrum. And extending to wavelengths longer and shorter than those of visible light, into the infra-red and ultra-violet wavelengths, the use of the spectroscope with photographic plates provided a source of information inaccessible to visual observation. In his famous Treatise, published in 1873, Clerk Maxwell was able to show that these light waves were not the only form of electromagnetic radiation, but that there must be a wide range of wavelengths either side of the optical spectrum. Inspired by Maxwell's work, Heinrich Hertz made his famous discovery of radio waves in 1887. It was a long time before astronomers could detect and use these radiations, but with Hertz's discovery, radio astronomy became a possibility.

When radio was only three years old, the first recorded suggestion of the science of radio astronomy was made. It was a tremendous leap in the dark, and it needed a genius to take it. Thomas Edison was the genius and the suggestion was made in a letter to Professor Holden, Principal of Lick Observatory in California, written on 2 November 1890 by Professor A. E. Kennelly. Professor Kennelly, who first predicted the existence of the terrestrial ionosphere, worked with Edison in his private laboratory. The letter contains this sentence:

17

Along with the electromagnetic disturbances we receive from the sun which of course you know we recognize as light and heat (I must apologize for stating facts you are so conversant with), it is not unreasonable to suppose that there will be disturbances of much longer wavelength. If so, we might translate them into sound.

The means of translation was bold and ingenious, and is explained in the letter, quoted now at greater length.

I may mention that Mr Edison, who does not confine himself to any single line of thought or action, has lately decided on turning a mass of iron ore in New Jersey, that is mined commercially, to account in the direction of research in Solar physics. Our time is, of course, occupied at the Laboratory in practical work, but on this instance the experiment will be a purely scientific one. The ore is magnetite, and is magnetic not so much on its own account like a separate steel magnet but rather by induction under the earth's polarity. It is only isolated blocks of the ore that acquire permanent magnetism in any degree. Along with the electromagnetic disturbances we receive from the sun which, of course, you know we recognize as light and heat (I must apologize for stating facts you are so conversant with), it is not unreasonable to suppose that there will be disturbances of much longer wavelength. If so, we might translate them into sound. Mr Edison's plan is to erect on poles round the bulk of the ore, a cable of seven carefully insulated wires, whose final terminals will be brought to a telephone or other apparatus. It is then possible that violent disturbances in the sun's atmosphere might so disturb either the normal electromagnetic flow of energy we receive, or the normal distribution of magnetic force on this planet, as to bring about an appreciably great change in the flow of magnetic induction embraced by the cable loop, enhanced and magnified as this should be by the magnetic condensation and conductivity of the ore body, which must comprise millions of tons.

Of course, it is impossible to say whether his anticipation will be realized until the plan is tried as we hope it will be in a few weeks. It occurred to me that, supposing any results were obtained indicating solar influence, we should not be able to establish the fact unless we have positive evidence of coincident disturbances in the corona. Perhaps, if you would, you could tell us at what moments such disturbances took place. I must confess I do not know whether sun spot changes enable such disturbances to be precisely recorded, or whether you keep any apparatus at work that can record changes in the corona independently of the general illumination. I have no doubt however that you could set us on the right track to determine the times of disturbance optically to compare with the indications of Mr Edison's receiver, assuming that it does record as we hope.

Of the experiment itself there appears to exist no record, except that, on 21 November, Kennelly writes that the poles have arrived ready to be set up. We may be sure, however, that no solar radiation was detected, for two good reasons. Firstly, very sensitive detectors are needed for even the strongest solar radio waves, and secondly, radiations of a wavelength long enough to be picked up by such an apparatus are prevented, by the terrestrial ionosphere, from reaching the earth. The experiment, though without hope of success, is admirable in its conception, and the idea that prompted it remains as the basis of a new science.

Although Edison was the first, he was certainly not the only famous scientist of the last century to attempt to pick up radio waves from the sun. In 1894 Sir Oliver Lodge said, in a lecture before the Royal Institution in London, that he was proposing 'to try for long wave radiation from the sun, filtering out the ordinary well-known waves by a blackboard, or other sufficiently opaque substance'. He reports the experiment in a book called *Signalling across Space without Wires:*

I did not succeed in this, for a sensitive coherer in an outside shed unprotected by the thick walls of a substantial building cannot be kept quiet for long. I found its spot of light liable to frequent weak and occasionally violent excursions, and I could not trace any of these to the influence of the sun. There were evidently too many terrestrial sources of disturbance in a city like Liverpool to make the experiment feasible. I don't know that it might not possibly be successful in some isolated country place; but clearly the arrangement must be highly sensitive in order to succeed.

He has our sympathy. Optical astronomers suffer from city street lights; radio astronomers suffer from city street trams, and, in these days, from far worse evils in the form of radio-communication transmitters, whose frequencies range through the whole available radio spectrum.

Leaving aside these early attempts, we can assign a birthday to our subject with an accuracy unusual in science. In the issue of the

Proceedings of the Institute of Radio Engineers of December 1932. Karl Jansky pubilshed an account of his historic first reception of radio waves from outer space. Had 1932 been a year of high sunspot activity, Jansky would undoubtedly have found the radiations from the sun for which Edison and Lodge had looked in vain. As it was, the sun was quiet, and instead the radio waves coming from our galaxy were discovered.

Jansky was carrying out for the Bell laboratories in America a study of the noise level to be expected when a sensitive short-wave radio receiver is used with a directional aerial system in long-distance communications. He was listening for crackling noises from thunderstorms, and he had an aerial system which could scan round the sky to find the direction from which these signals came. It was rather a clumsy contraption, mounted on Ford model T motor wheels for easy rotation. The noise level was found never to decrease below a certain level, but this level varied gradually through the day. When Jansky listened on an ordinary loudspeaker to the output from his receiver, he heard only a steady hissing sound, quite different in character from the crackles of thunderstorms.

Jansky found that the greatest signal always occurred when the aerial pointed in a certain direction in space, that is in a direction fixed relative to the stars, and not relative to the earth or even to the sun. This direction turned out to be the direction of the centre of our galaxy, where there is the greatest concentration of stars, and Jansky was able to say, without any doubt, that he was listening to signals 'broadcast' from the Milky Way.

Jansky's discovery was well publicized in America. Alongside the technical reports there were newspaper reports, and even a radio programme broadcasting to the people of America the recorded hissing sound that came from Jansky's receiver. Surprisingly enough, however, the subject was dropped almost completely after Jansky had carried through the original plan of his experiment, and it was not until after the Second World War that radio astronomy was established as a separate science, and started its spectacular growth.

One radio amateur bridged the gap between Jansky's first discovery of radio signals received from outer space, and the postwar surge into the new science. This was Grote Reber, who for several years was the only radio astronomer in the world. He is still a radio astronomer, and he is still a pioneer, exploring new branches of the subject with the same enthusiasm which he once applied to amateur short-wave radio, and then to the construction of the first radio-telescope.

Reber accepted Karl Jansky's work as an opportunity and a challenge. He built for himself, in his spare time, with his own resources and in his own back yard in Wheaton, Illinois, a steer-able parabolic reflector, 30 feet in diameter. This he used, with sensitive receivers, to make some remarkable recordings of cosmic radio waves.

After many disappointments, he found that he could record the 'cosmic static', discovered by Jansky at a wavelength of 15 metres, on the much shorter wavelengths of 60 cm., where his new radio telescope was able to give precise details of the direction of origin of the radio waves. In his maps, which in many details remained unsurpassed for fifteen years, it is possible to see for the first time startling differences between the visible sky and the radio sky. Nothing could be seen of radio waves from any visible object, except the sun, but peaks of emission were to be seen in various parts of the Milky Way where there was no reason to expect them. Some of these peaks we can now recognize as the radio stars in the constellations of Cassiopeia, Cygnus, and Taurus. Reber recognized the importance of his experiments, and in papers published in 1940 he showed quite clearly that a new branch of astronomy was in being.

Reber's results were published in 1940 and 1942, when the attention of most scientists was directed elsewhere than towards pure research. Nevertheless, his papers were not ignored, and towards the end of the war his results were gathered together with several interesting new observations made as a by-product of research in radar, and used as a stepping stone towards the beginning of radio astronomy as we now know it.

The contribution of radar research came largely through the work of one man, J. S. Hey. His wartime job was in the Army Operational Research Group, where with his colleagues he studied reports of the efficiency of all the army radar equipments, and investigated all the reports of jamming by enemy transmitters. From these reports came the first indication that the sun could transmit radio waves in the metre wavelength region. This radiation, as we shall see, was radiation from an active sunspot, and it was the following up of this clue by new radio observatories at Sydney and at Cambridge that started the extensive work on the radio emission from the sun, both from spots and from the surface of the 'quiet' sun.

A second result from wartime radar experience was the detection of radar echoes from meteor trails. Hey and his colleagues were able to continue work with army radar sets immediately after the war, and to follow up reports of short-lived echoes whose association with meteors was only conjectural. Hey showed that every meteor leaves a trail of ionization in the upper atmosphere, which reflects radio waves as effectively as a long metallic wire. The operational necessity of tracking down the source of unwanted radar echoes was soon replaced by the driving curiosity of scientific investigation, for Hey found that the echoes not only could be used as a means of exploring the upper atmosphere but that they also revealed the existence of concentrated streams of meteors of greater intensity than any previously seen.

Hey's third contribution came as the result of an experiment planned from the outset as a work of observational radio astronomy. Following Jansky and Reber, he decided to plot out the cosmic radio waves over the sky with the best aerial system available. He soon had a map of the radio emission from the Northern sky, showing the Milky Way as its most prominent feature. But in one spot in the constellation of Cygnus he found a fluctuating signal, which he interpreted correctly as a radio signal from a discrete source. As was shown later, the fluctuations were imposed on the signal by the terrestrial ionosphere, while the source itself was a steady and powerful transmitter. It was some years before it was identified with the exciting object known as Cygnus A, the most distant and the most powerful radio transmitter known.

Hey occupies a very special place in the history of radio astronomy. He was responsible for three major discoveries, which must be reckoned as about half the major discoveries of the whole subject. The debt owed to him by astronomy has recently been recognized by the award of the Eddington Medal of the Royal Astronomical Society. He is still actively engaged in radio astronomy.

After the publication of Hey's work the progress of radio astronomy was very rapid, and it remains so. It is strange that so little was done in America, where the ideas were first born and where the first observations were made, but it is nevertheless true that for several years the main development was in Sydney, Australia, under J. L. Pawsey, and in Cambridge, England, under M. Ryle. Both groups remain pre-eminent, but they are joined by observatories all over the world, and we now see such a resurgence of radio astronomy in America that we may find in a very few years time that it is competition between the U.S.A. and the U.S.S.R. in constructing giant radio telescopes that determines the main lines of progress. In the meantime the initiative, and the competition, is spread widely over the whole world, and the volume of research in radio astronomy, and its scope, increase from year to year at a rate undreamed of only a few years ago.

CHAPTER 2

The Radio Universe

WHEN we look up at the sky on a clear night we look into a vast mystery. Our eyes receive as points of light the radiations from a myriad of stars, and as wonder turns to inquiry we realize that these radiations contain all the information we can ever receive from the visible universe. With reservations perhaps inside our own solar system, we cannot touch any part of it, we cannot perform experiments on it; we can only look at it.

The radio astronomer looking out into the universe receives the electromagnetic radiations known as radio waves instead of light. Although he uses complex instruments for analysing these radio waves, he still adopts the language of the visual observer, and talks of what he 'sees' with his radio telescope. He can build up a picture of the universe, a radio universe, just as real and meaningful as the familiar visible universe. Where the two pictures differ, they in fact complement one another. Together they provide our only knowledge of the universe around us, and we must at the outset recognize the limits of our perception. The limits are so narrow that we may doubt the reality of the fantastic universe so imperfectly revealed.

Dr Johnson, when he was confronted with the argument that a stone could not be said positively to exist except as an impression in his brain, so that all that he could logically say about the stone was that he *thought* he saw it, said 'I refute it thus', and kicked the stone. No refutation really, but only a demonstration that all our knowledge of nature comes via our senses, normally more than one sense. For proof of the existence of the stone, the sense of touch is almost as good as the sense of sight. Our total detailed information on the nature of the stone, and of any other physical object, depends very much on the different senses we use in our inquiry about it, and on the way in which those senses are used. Putting it in a different way, physics is the acquisition and marshalling of information about the universe, and in all parts of

24

physics the first emphasis must be on the nature of experimental observations and their interpretation. What is the nature of the information available to astronomy?

The whole science of visual astronomy has grown from optical observations of light radiated from heavenly bodies, and this light brings information in several ways. Firstly the bodies can be hot, and shine with their own light. The quality and quantity of this radiation tells us much of the composition and the temperature of its source. Secondly light may be absorbed, perhaps totally, as when Venus or Mercury is observed in transit across the disc of the sun, or perhaps only partially, indicating the existence of a cloud of gas or dust in space. When light is partially absorbed, it is often found that its quality, or colour, is changed, and also that its spectrum shows absorption lines. The extent of the absorption, and the changes in the spectrum, give information about the absorbing medium. Thirdly, light can also be reflected, either specularly or diffusely; by reflection of sunlight we are able to see the planets and the moon, and by the reflection of starlight we are able to see some of the nebulae in our Galaxy which have not enough energy to shine with their own light.

Lastly, light can suffer refraction, between its source in the heavens, and our eyes or optical instruments. This 'bending' of the light waves takes place in the earth's atmosphere and may be a nuisance in optical astronomy, but in studying the terrestrial atmosphere, the random refraction and diffraction effects which make the stars twinkle can be turned to good account.

As well as the light waves from the sun, moon, stars, and planets, there are two kinds of visitors to this planet from outer space, bringing their own rather more direct information. These are the meteors and the cosmic rays; both interest the radio astronomer as keenly as they interest the conventional astronomer.

Knowledge gained by radio astronomy must come via channels similar to those of optical astronomy, i.e. radiation, absorption, reflection, and refraction. The essential difference in the kind of information received is that the regions and objects which radiate, absorb, reflect, or refract radio waves, appear often to be very different from the objects of the visible universe. Using radio waves, we can 'see' such invisible objects as a cloud of electrons, or of transparent hydrogen gas.

The Ionosphere

Our first example of an invisible object revealed to us by radio waves must be the ionosphere. This cloud of electrons, 100 miles or so above the earth's surface, is invisible, but nevertheless reflects long-wavelength radio signals so effectively that broadcasts from Australia can be heard in this country, after they have bounced round the earth inside a kind of spherical mirror. If the ionosphere reflected or absorbed light waves with such efficiency we could have no visual knowledge of the universe around us, and this world would be a very different place.

At the time of a solar flare, the reflection of radio waves by the ionosphere is spoilt by absorption in the lowest ionized regions, and when this happens radio communications can be severed so completely that ships may lose contact with the land. Submarines at sea have in fact been reported lost for many hours and searches started which were only called off when the 'fadeout' passed. These 'fadeouts' have a close connexion with the radio emission from the sun.

The ionosphere also refracts radio waves, sometimes in a very complicated way, and with the obvious importance of radio communication it is not surprising that much research is devoted to its study. The earliest work on ionosphere refraction was with the effect of the ionosphere on man-made radio waves generated on this planet, but more recently attention has been turned to those generated outside the earth both from natural extra-terrestrial sources and from man-made earth satellites. Just as atmospheric scintillation is a nuisance to optical astronomy, so the ionosphere is a nuisance to radio astronomy. Fortunately, as its properties depend on the wavelengths of the radio waves it is not entirely impenetrable. In Figure 1 the spectrum of electromagnetic waves is displayed, showing the two ranges which are transmitted through the atmosphere and ionosphere without absorption or reflection. These two ranges of penetrating electromagnetic waves are the two 'windows' through which we can 'look' at the universe. The optical window is limited by the absorption in the atmosphere of light in the extreme ultra-violet and infra-red, while the radio window is limited at one end where it meets the infra-red at wavelengths of about 1 centimetre, and at the other end where

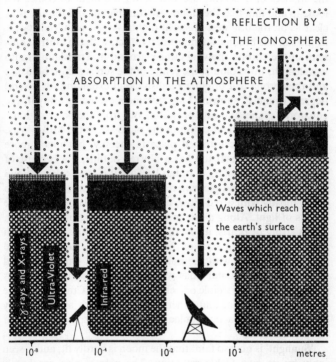

REFLECTION BY THE IONOSPHERE

ABSORPTION IN THE ATMOSPHERE

Waves which reach the earth's surface

γ-rays and X-rays

Ultra-Violet

Infra-red

| 10^{-8} | 10^{-4} | 10^{-2} | 10^{2} | metres |

1. The spectrum of electromagnetic waves. Only two bands of wavelengths, light and radio, can penetrate the terrestrial atmosphere and ionosphere

wavelengths longer than about 10 metres are reflected by the ionosphere. From 1 metre to 10 metres wavelength there is an ionospheric phenomenon which occasionally impairs our clear vision, the 'scintillation' of radio stars.

Looking out now at the radio universe beyond the terrestrial atmosphere, we may imagine that our eyes are no longer sensitive to light, and that we can see radio waves instead. Let us also imagine that it is daytime, and that the sky is overcast so that the optical astronomers are able to relax, perhaps disappointed that the chances of observing are slender for the night to come. We look up and find that the clouds are transparent and the sky is as clear as on the brightest of starlit nights. And it is indeed starlit, as the sun has become a strange dim object, with the blurred outlines of the corona showing clearly around it. Translating radio wavelengths into colours, the centre of the sun is a faint blue disc and the corona is a brighter reddish cloud extending for several degrees round it, showing long streamers extending away in the equatorial plane, and rays projecting out from the polar region.

The most prominent object in the radio sky is the Milky Way. We see it in its accustomed place in the sky, but much more clearly than before. It too has a blurred outline, not because of the many separate stars in it, but because it is itself a large cloud of gas, radiating and glowing red. In it we see some bright radio stars, mostly with a red glow, and appreciably larger than mere points of light. Along a line in the centre of the Milky Way lies, like a string of pearls, a row of shining blue clouds. We look in vain for the familiar stars of the Plough, Orion, Taurus; instead the sky is covered with thousands of new stars. Only a detailed comparison with a star atlas would show that some of the less conspicuous of the visible objects are there – the Crab nebula, the Andromeda nebula, and others, most of which are not really stars, but extra-galactic nebulae in the depths of space beyond our own star system.

'Sunlight' is now so faint that the moon is hardly lit, and is seen only by its own feeble radiation. The planets also are barely visible, except for Jupiter, which is spasmodically sending out flashes of red light, as though a violent thunderstorm were raging on its surface.

Thermal Radiation

Why does the sky look so different for 'radio eyes'? It must first be realized that most of the difference lies not in an unnatural

28

dimness of the familiar objects, but in an unexpected brightness of unfamiliar ones. The dependence upon wavelength of the radiation from a hot body has been known, as far as long wavelengths are concerned, since the work of Rayleigh and Jeans in 1905. This may be summarized in the statements:

(i) the energy per unit wavelength range is inversely proportional to the fourth power of the wavelength;

(ii) the energy per unit frequency range is proportional to the square of the frequency.

Now, as the wavelength of cosmic radio waves is up to 10 million times greater than that of light waves, this law tells us to expect very little indeed in the way of radiation from the sun, or any other hot body, at radio wavelengths.

Little as it is, this thermal radiation can be detected from the sun's surface at very short radio wavelengths, and its strength is determined by the temperature of the surface, or photosphere. Here the 'radio sun' is very like the visible sun. At longer radio wavelengths the solar corona plays a dominant part and becomes the only 'visible' part of the sun. Now the sun takes on a quite different appearance. The corona is an extensive atmosphere, largely composed of hot hydrogen. It is made familiar to us by photographs of the sun taken at times of total eclipse, when the hydrogen atmosphere of the sun is seen brilliantly lit from the surface of the sun below (see Plate 8B). The hydrogen is totally ionized, broken up by the intense sunlight into photons and electrons.

It is the electrons which are responsible for the radio appearance of the sun, and it is the corona rather than the photosphere which can be explored by radio waves. This corona is at a temperature of a million degrees, while that of the photosphere is a mere 6,000° K.

The string of clouds along the equator of the galaxy, running through the centre of the Milky Way, also radiate because they contain a hot electron gas. These are clouds of ionized hydrogen surrounding some particularly hot stars which provide the energy for their radiation. Hydrogen is the commonest element in the universe, and a tenuous hydrogen gas pervades the whole galaxy. It has normally very little energy, as one might except in the cold depths of galactic space, but here and there it comes under the influence of an energetic young star in the earlier stages of its evolution, radiating the strongly ionizing ultra-violet light waves. The gas is then broken up into protons and electrons, and these acquire considerable energies. These clouds of ionized hydrogen are called the 'H II regions', like the ones photographed in Plates 5 and 6B, and they are much larger than the solar corona. The temperature of the gas is only about 10,000° K, and the density is very small – about 10 atoms per cubic centimetre – but the thermal radiation is still sufficient to make these clouds prominent objects at short radio wavelengths. They are practically the only celestial objects which have a similar appearance for radio as for visible light.

Non-Thermal Radiation

The thermal radiation which enables our radio eyes to see the sun and planets, and the H II clouds, by virtue of their temperature alone is no more than could be expected from optical observations of the same objects. The startling features in the radio sky are objects quite unfamiliar to optical astronomy, again radiating because they contain very energetic electrons, but not as a result of being hot in the usual sense. A broadcasting station sends out radio waves because of the energetic electrons in its transmitting aerials, but it does not have to be hot to achieve this.

The nearest source of such non-thermal radiation is the sun. There is at all times a steady thermal radiation from the corona, radiating according to its million degrees over a region 2 million miles across, but the sun can easily beat this with a blast of radiation from a single sunspot.

These sunspots appear on the visible surface of the sun as dark regions. They are dark because they have a temperature lower than their surroundings. But when sunspots appear on the sun's disc, the radio emission on long wavelengths may increase by more than a thousandfold. When this happens, our radio picture of a large blurred hot corona becomes lost in the glare of a brilliant flickering radiation from the atmosphere above the sunspot. The physical conditions here are difficult to determine, but it is certain that particles with high energies are involved, and certain too, and more important, that there is a large magnetic field.

Sunspot radiation is not thermal radiation. The corona above a sunspot is no hotter than anywhere else, and may even be cooler. But there are some remarkable processes going on here, in which energy is fed into the corona in a way similar to that in which an electric dynamo feeds power into a radio transmitter. The solar dynamo is seen in any photograph of a sunspot, whose contorted outlines follow lines of magnetic field which change and move violently during the life of the spot. Electric fields are generated, which can accelerate charged particles just as electrons are accelerated through radio valves. The rest of the analogy is not so clear, but in some way this dynamo energy becomes converted into radio waves whose strength bears no relation to the temperature of the gas where they are generated.

Non-thermal radiation is responsible for the whole brilliance of the radio sky, providing all of its unfamiliar features. The Milky Way, which is the disc of our Galaxy seen from near one edge, produces radio waves from interstellar gas which may be at a temperature of 100° K (minus 173° C): penetrating this gas is a flux of high-energy particles which radiate very much more powerfully. These particles must be part of the cosmic rays, observed on earth by their passage through photographic plates, or cloud chambers, and other detecting devices familiar to atomic physics. In a sense their radio radiation is thermal, as its energy derives from the individual motions of these electrons which have a kind of temperature of their own; but there is here no real thermal equilibrium between the radiation and any body of hot gas. The meaning of temperature for these most tenuous gases must be regarded as of a somewhat academic interest anyway, but the distinction between the energies of the cosmic rays and of the cold and sluggish gas through which they pass is obvious.

In the galactic plane there are some especially active spots forming discrete sources of radio waves, and these again are non-thermal radiators. The energy supply for these is fairly evident, as many of them are visible nebulae which are the remains of exploding stars. The visible wisps of gas produced by these supernova explosions are still blowing outwards at some hundreds of miles per second. One such nebula, the Crab nebula in Taurus, contains cosmic ray electrons which are such powerful generators of non-thermal radiation that they produce visible light in addition to radio waves.

Looking further out into space, the radio sky contains many bright nebulae, each of which is a complete galaxy of stars like our own. Some, like our own Galaxy, radiate strongly by virtue of the electrons circulating throughout the interstellar space; others, which may be seen at very much greater distances because of their greater power, derive their energy from the kinetic energy of two complete galaxies in collision. These are the distant radio stars which are the most exciting features of the whole radio sky, for it seems that they may be so powerful that they can be seen even beyond the distance covered by the 200-inch telescope of Mt Palomar, and they may be the only means of revealing to us the structure of most distant parts of the universe.

The Solar System

Nearer to earth, the appearance of the solar system to radio eyes contains few surprises apart from the sun itself. The corona of the sun does, however, manifest itself in a rather peculiar way at great distances from the sun itself, where the coronal gas is so thin that it emits practically no radio waves. On long radio wavelengths this tenuous gas appears as a haze in a large volume round the sun, rather like the heat haze to be seen over the surface of roads in summertime. The haziness comes from irregularities in the corona, and these irregularities can be investigated by observing the blurred outline of radio stars seen through the haze.

The planets appear as faintly self-luminous bodies, and their emission only enables us to measure their surface temperature. The same is true of the moon. But one planet, Jupiter, is most surprisingly a source of intense bursts of radio emission, in some way like the radio 'atmospherics' produced by lightning flashes. The explanation is not at all clear, but the phenomenon provides an excellent example of the difference between the optical and radio skies. On the one hand, the usual view of Jupiter through a telescope gives a fairly detailed picture of its surface, showing quite complicated markings and colours. On the other hand, radio astronomy enables only an average surface temperature to be found, with no detail at all. To compensate for this, the atmosphere of Jupiter, quite transparent to light, shows up to radio astronomers as a most lively and interesting place, with an ionosphere like our own, and with a magnetic field whose existence was previously undetected.

Jupiter embodies the difference between optical and radio astronomy, and shows how nicely the two disciplines complement one another. It is now the task of the radio astronomer to observe the new universe that has suddenly become accessible to him, and to fit all his new observations into the frame of the visible universe that the labours of conventional astronomers have so carefully and exactly delineated. It is hard to say where the effect of our newly expanded vision will be greatest; each radio astronomer will have his own view depending on his own interests. In the mind of the author and of his colleagues at Cambridge, there is a strong conviction that the great contribution of radio astronomy to the understanding of the universe lies not in fields already accessible to optical astronomy, but beyond them in the furthermost reaches of observable space. Here, as we shall see, light becomes a feebler and feebler tool as distances increase, and in comparison the usefulness of radio becomes progressively greater. It seems very probable that already we have within our grasp the tools of exploration into the most fundamental problem ever to challenge the thoughts of mankind – the problem of the origin of the universe itself.

CHAPTER 3

The Sun as a Radio Transmitter

THE sun must be accounted to be the most important of the heavenly bodies which illuminate the radio sky. The radio sun is not so prominent as the visible sun, nor indeed do its radio waves directly affect our daily lives except as indicators of solar disturbances, which in turn may affect radio communications or compass bearings on earth. Nevertheless it is an extraordinarily rewarding object to study by radio, as it is so very variable in its behaviour. It is the only ordinary star in the sky to be seen by radio, and it is the only known variable 'radio star'. The sun is not an uncommon type of star; there must be many millions of G-type stars like the sun in the Galaxy, but the next nearest one to the earth is so much further away that its radio waves are undetectable.

The sun represents a laboratory where conditions quite unrealizable on earth are accessible to our radio telescopes. Different parts of the sun have different conditions; we can at any time look at radiation from the surface at a temperature only existing on earth in the fireball of a nuclear explosion, or we can observe the effect of electrons spiralling freely round lines of magnetic force in a gas more rarified than the best laboratory vacuum. The radio waves these electrons emit are often the only clue to their very existence, and the only indication of the forces which accelerate them to energies sometimes as high as those of cosmic rays. We shall see how it is that by measuring the radio waves emitted by the sun and the corona around it that we are able to explore a wide range of physical conditions, and to connect some of the spectacular events on the sun with geophysical phenomena such as aurorae and magnetic storms.

The radio transmitters which broadcast the B.B.C. programmes do so by generating oscillating electric currents in aerial wires held high above the ground, so that the radio waves are launched efficiently into space. The electric currents themselves consist of moving clouds of electrons in wires, or in electric discharges. It is the art of the radio engineer to regiment these movements in ways which do not produce heat, like current in an electric fire, but which produce radio waves from cold aerial wires.

In the solar atmosphere, the temperature is so high that the hydrogen gas of which it is largely composed is dissociated into protons and electrons, which are then kept in rapid motion by virtue of this same high temperature. It is for this reason not surprising that the sun is a radio transmitter, and indeed that it is the most outstanding radio transmitter in the sky. No self-respecting radio engineer would, however, encourage such physical conditions, in which the electron motions are entirely disorganized, moving in all directions in complete chaos. The difference from the orderly oscillation in a transmitting aerial is reflected in the difference in the radiation; oscillation at one chosen frequency produces only that one frequency of radiation, while random motion produces at once every frequency in the radio spectrum, with the energy of the electron gas spread widely instead of concentrated in frequency as it must be in a radio broadcasting station.

There are two main kinds of solar radiation. Sometimes the sun is said to be 'quiet', when there are few sunspots and no flares to be seen. More usually it is 'active', with a very wide repertoire of behaviour. The quiet sun is a complicated enough radio transmitter, but, as we shall see in later chapters, the active sun outdoes it in every way – in spectacle, in complication, and in defiance of theory. The quiet sun is reasonably well understood, and the story told by the radio waves it transmits agrees with the story told by the light waves, and supplements it in a most satisfactory way.

Radio Waves from the Quiet Sun

One of the most startling and important features of the solar atmosphere is the extremely high temperature – about 1 million degrees absolute – which is maintained through the whole of the outer regions (the corona). This fact became an accepted one, on optical evidence, at about the same time as the first radio observations of the sun were being made.

The visible surface of the sun, called the photosphere, is at a temperature of 6,000° K, and is surrounded by the chromosphere, a region several thousands of miles thick, which is at about 20,000° K. No one would reasonably expect to find temperatures of a million degrees further away than these regions from the sun's centre. For the source of all solar energy lies in the very depths of the sun, where hydrogen is being converted into helium at the rate of 500 million tons per second, and heat flows out to the surface by radiation from atom to atom inside the sun. There is a steady gradient of temperature all the way from 10 millon degrees at the centre to 6,000° K on the surface.

The temperature of the corona was originally measured by spectroscopy. Two methods were used, the first being a study of the Fraunhofer absorption lines which have already been mentioned in Chapter 1. The details of these lines show that the atoms responsible for them are in violent motion, giving the line a width which is increased by the Doppler effect. The velocities deduced from the width of the line correspond to the thermal motions expected from a corona at a temperature of 10^6 °K.

In the second spectroscopic method some spectral lines were observed in light emitted by the corona, the wavelengths of these lines being characteristic, not only of the atoms, but of their state of ionization, which is in turn dependent upon the temperature. In this dependence lies the solution to a long standing mystery of some of the so-called 'coronal lines', which do not correspond with any which could be produced in the laboratory. The mystery of these lines was at one time such that they were supposed to originate in atoms of a new unknown element, named coronium. It has now been found that the coronal lines come from the highly ionized atoms of several quite ordinary heavy elements, such as iron in the form known as Fe XIV, which is an iron atom which has lost no less than thirteen electrons as a result of the high temperature of its surroundings. (Spectroscopists designate an unionized atom by the Roman I, adding to this for each electron lost.) Accepting this evidence for the temperature, and other optical evidence for the density of the corona, we might fairly expect the sun to look like a large, blurred, million-degree radio emitter, at all radio wavelengths.

The first careful measurement of the temperature of the source of solar radio radiations gave an answer of 6,000° K, which is the photospheric temperature. This measurement was made by Southworth in 1942. Later the result was corrected to 18,000° K. but even this is much less than 10^6 °K. The result occasioned no surprise at the time, for the high temperature of the corona was

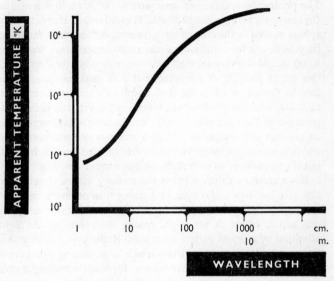

2. Graph showing how high-temperature radio waves are emitted by the corona at long wavelengths, while the shorter radio waves emitted by the chromosphere and photosphere correspond to lower temperatures

not yet widely accepted. Southworth's work was done on very short wavelengths, between 1 and 10 cm., and this proved later to contain the explanation of the low temperatures. Later work on longer wavelengths, particularly on wavelengths longer than about 50 cm. (i.e. of radio frequency less than 600 Mc/s), gave results which, if expressed in the same terms, do indeed indicate temperatures in the region of a million degrees.

The graph in Figure 2 shows the variation in apparent temperature of the quiet sun over the radio spectrum. Broadly speaking, at the shorter wavelengths the temperature is near to that of the photosphere, and at the longest, to that of the corona. The difference shows a difference in origin, and the reason is not hard to find. The corona is completely transparent for short wavelengths, just as it is for light. Radio waves are generated in any hot body, and their intensities correspond to the temperature of the body. The photosphere, therefore, generates 6,000° K radio waves, and the chromosphere generates 20,000° K radio waves. If the chromosphere as well as the corona were transparent for radio waves, as they both are for light waves, the radio temperature would be 6,000° K. At the very shortest radio wavelengths, less than 1 cm., this might possibly be observed, but it is usual at short wavelengths to find that it is the chromosphere which is the effective radiator, with the photosphere hidden behind it. The radio temperature is then around 20,000° K. On long wavelengths, the corona not only plays the part of a screen which prevents radio waves from the photosphere and chromosphere from reaching us, but it also radiates its own million-degree radio waves.

If we are now to press home the analogy between seeing the sky with our new radio eyes, and seeing it in ordinary light, we must specify the wavelength of radio waves which our new eyes will admit, rather as we might specify the colour of the light admitted by a tinted pair of spectacles. Radio eyes working at a long wavelength would see the sun as a large flaming cloud completely obscuring the familiar sphere; for short wavelength eyes the sphere is only slightly changed, being a little larger and marked with streaks and blobs corresponding to the well-known sunspots and other optical markings. At each wavelength the intensity of the radiation betrays the temperature of the region which is seen to be emitting.

The Brightness Distribution across the Sun

As well as the apparent variation of temperature of the sun with wavelength, we find a variation of the size of the source of solar radiations according to the wavelength at which measurements are made. Again using the idea of radio eyes, it is as though the source is large for red light and small for blue. The solar corona is several degrees across, and the photosphere only half a degree. Furthermore, the corona is not just one thin shell, but an electron cloud whose density falls steadily with height. As the density falls, the wavelength at which the corona can absorb radio waves increases. The absorbing sphere is not a single shell but contains layer upon layer of different densities and temperatures, rather like the skins of an onion. By observing on progressively shorter and shorter and shorter wavelengths, we may peel off the successive layers of the onion, examining each as we go down deeper. At each stage the size of the sun will be different, depending on the wavelength. This possibility of exploring the sun's corona, by measuring the distribution of 'brightness' across the radio sun at a variety of wavelengths, presents a real challenge to the radio astronomer, offering him information that is practically denied to optical astronomers. In this way he may investigate the variation of both electron density and temperature with height above the photosphere. Let us see how the radio telescope is applied to this problem.

This measurement is not at all easy. Radio telescopes differ from optical telescopes in various rather obvious ways, such as the use of wire mesh instead of glass for reflecting radio waves instead of light. Two more fundamental differences are that the radio telescope cannot take photographs, and that the radio telescope has such poor angular resolving power that all but the more elaborate instruments would only be able to tell us the diameter of the sun to within the beamwidth of an ordinary aerial, which might be 3° or more for long wavelengths. It is like exploring the sky by using a pin hole camera, in which the image is detected by a photocell instead of a photographic plate.

In measuring the angular diameters of visible stars Michelson used an interferometer system, to give greatly increased accuracy of angular measurement. The same system can be used to increase the resolving power of radio telescopes, and this method has been applied to the problem of measuring the brightness distribution across the sun. Here we must anticipate Chapter 18, and describe briefly what is meant by a radio interferometer.

A radio interferometer consists of two separate aerials, each receiving radiation from the sun, joined together to the same receiver. Figure 3 shows the effect on the reception characteristics,

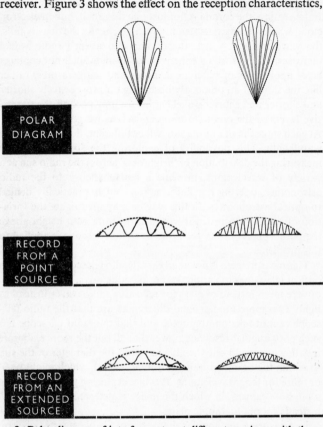

3. Polar diagram of interferometer at different spacings, with the records produced from two types of source

or 'polar diagram' of the aerials. As the earth rotates, and the sun moves through the polar diagram of the aerials, the received signal varies in a way dependent on the aerial spacing: i.e. slowly for small spacing, rapidly for large spacings, as the sun moves over undulations in the reception pattern. But if the pattern is made very fine, by putting the aerials a long way apart, the sun may be too large to fit into or between the undulations, and the received signal will no longer fall to zero between the pattern lobes. Here, then, is a method of measuring the size of the radio sun at various wavelengths, even though only quite small aerials need be used. It is possible, in this way, even to measure details of the brightness distribution across the sun, and this has now been done over a range of wavelengths from 8 m. to 1·4 m. At the shorter wavelength of 21 cm., a special multiple interferometer

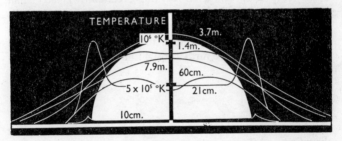

4. Distribution of radio brightness across the sun at various wavelengths. The longer wavelengths are generated far out in the corona, which is at 10^6°K; the shorter wavelengths come from the cooler chromosphere. The 21-cm. curve shows 'limb brightening', typical of short wavelengths

using thirty-two aerials simultaneously has been used in Australia for this work, and at 10 cm. a single aerial, large enough to resolve the sun itself, has been in use in Canada for some time.

Figure 4 shows the sections of the radio sun obtained with these various aerial systems. The brightness temperature of the surface is plotted against distance from the centre of the solar disc, using the radius of the photosphere as a unit. The progressive change in temperature and shape with wavelength can be seen here, with the broad diffuse corona giving way to the sharper disc of short wavelengths. An additional feature of the sun at short wavelengths is the bright region near its edges. This 'limb brightening' is to be expected at those wavelengths where the cooler photosphere can be seen near the centre of the sun. Near the edges, a greater depth of the hot corona is to be found in the line of sight, giving an increased brightness in a ring just outside the visible limb of the sun. At 60 cm., limb brightening only occurs across the solar equator, and not near the poles, while at shorter wavelengths it makes a complete bright ring round the sun. The radio corona has now been explored by this means out to the very low densities of 10^7 electrons per c.c., which may be compared with the 10^{23} molecules in each c.c. of air at the earth's surface. Even at this low density the temperature is very high, certainly greater than 100,000° K, and we have certainly not reached the end of the corona. Before describing another way of looking at the corona further out again, let us return to the chromosphere, where eclipses of the sun give further insight into the state of the electrons there.

Solar Eclipses

The most remarkable coincidence to be found in the sky is that the moon and the sun subtend very nearly the same angle, $\frac{1}{2}$°, at the earth. Consequently when it happens, as it occasionally does, that the moon comes between the earth and the sun, it just fits over the photosphere, affording a spectacular view of the light from the corona to those fortunate enough to be at the right place, at the right time, always provided that the weather is good enough (see Plate 8B). Expeditions to observe solar eclipses would not be nearly so important if the fit of the moon over the sun were less exact, which is the case for the radio sun. At long wavelengths the radio sun appears to be several degrees across, as it is the corona itself which generates the radio waves. It is only at shorter wavelengths, where the chromosphere or photosphere are concerned, that a significant eclipse can be observed. For wavelengths between 1 and 10 cm., the fit is not too bad, and the moon can cover up to about 90 per cent of the radio sun. The progressive drop in the radio waves reaching the earth as the moon covers up a larger and larger area delineates the details of the distribution of emission across the sun.

Some beautiful experimental results have been obtained in these radio eclipses, some when the sky was overcast, so that optical work was impossible. There are stories of astronomers who have attended as many as six solar eclipses, at all of which cloud spoilt their measurements. They must envy the radio

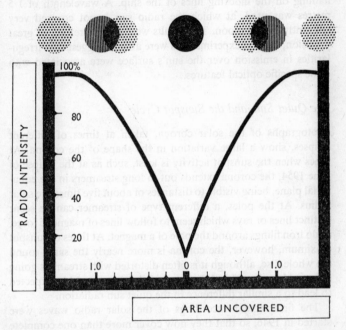

5. Radio eclipse of 30 June 1954. The eclipse was observed in Sweden by Mayer, Sloanaker, and Hagen, using a wavelength of 9·4 cm. The curve shows the experimental result as the sun was progressively covered and uncovered by the moon

astronomer his independence on weather. Figure 5 shows an eclipse curve, made on the wavelength of 9·4 cm.

The first radio eclipse observations hold an interesting place in the history of radio astronomy. They were made by Russian scientists at the eclipse of 20 May 1947. Two main problems of eclipse observation, the transport of rather large aerials to the observing site, and the directing of this aerial towards the sun, were solved by the masterly stroke of installing the whole apparatus on shipboard. The aerial consisted of ninety-six dipoles over a reflecting sheet, and as it was fixed to the ship, it was directed by hauling on the mooring lines of the ship. A wavelength of 1·5 metres was used, at which the radio sun is not covered very efficiently by the moon. The results were not, therefore, of great precision, but the experimenters were able to suggest that irregularities in emission over the sun's surface were associated with osme specific optical features.

The Quiet Sun, and the Sunspot Cycle

Photographs of the solar corona, taken at times of different eclipses, show a large variation in the shape of the corona. At times when the sunspot activity is least, such as at the eclipse of June 1954, the corona extends out in long streamers in the equatorial plane, being visible to distances of about five times the solar radius. At the poles, a different type of streamer can be seen: distinct lines or rays which seem to follow lines of magnetic force, as do iron filings around the pole of a magnet. At times of sunspot maximum, however, the corona is more nearly the same round the whole disc, although it is often distorted with streamers going off at odd angles. This difference in behaviour would be expected to lead to a similar difference in the quiet sun radiation.

The first regular recordings of the solar radio waves were started in 1946, so that they now cover more than one complete sunspot cycle of eleven years. Variations are certainly found, but it is hard to say whether the whole basic level of radiation changes, as the extra radiation coming from obvious disturbances on the sun masks any variations of this basic level. In other words, the sun is never really quiet during 'sunspot maximum' years. This extra radiation comes not only from the spectacular disturbances on the sun, noise storms, and flares (discussed in the next chapter), but seems to be associated with the regions rather curiously known as 'calcium plages'. These are areas of optical disturbance marked by the unusual emission of spectral lines from calcium, and are a common and long-lived feature of the sun. The long series of recordings gives us good ground for associating them with radio emission, particularly on wavelengths of about 50 cm. There are large cyclic variations of both the radio emission and the exposed area of calcium plage as the sun rotates, and the variations match one another very closely.

These areas, by the way, are also known as 'plages faculaires' and as 'faculae'. It is perhaps time that the nomenclature became standardized, preferably not on such an odd hybrid as 'calcium plage areas'.

Calcium plages are of further importance as being the apparent seat of the dramatic and more short-lived phenomena which are usually associated with the active sun. There is also a suspicion that they may be areas from which the sun replenishes its loss of coronal material by evaporation. The replenishment may only be significant at the time of solar flares; nevertheless the problem of maintaining the corona at all must be considered, and emission of large amounts of hot gas from the active parts of the surface seems not unlikely.

The difficulty of explaining the steady maintainance of the solar corona in its present state is considerable. Firstly it has to be heated to a million degrees, from a source of energy whose surface is only at 6,000° K. Secondly it must not 'boil off' faster than it can be replenished. 'Boiling off' occurs when the most energetic of the particles in the corona have sufficient velocity to escape from the sun's gravitational field. Our own atmosphere is boiling off slowly, although the common gases are not much affected; the lighter gases tend to be lost faster, otherwise helium would certainly be a common gas. The moon, being lighter and hence exerting less gravitational pull, can retain no atmosphere at all. The sun has a gravitational force at its surface twenty-seven times that of terrestrial gravity, but the corona is three thousand times as hot as our atmosphere and extends far out into space, so that boiling off is nevertheless quite possible. Energy for heating the corona could have come from this strong gravitational field, as matter could be attracted to the sun and fall into it with high velocities. This is called the 'accretion' theory of heating. A more generally accepted theory at present is that the energy comes from the high-temperature regions inside the sun, and is transmitted not directly as heat, but as mechanical oscillations. These waves are rather like sound waves, but involve also the magnetic field of the sun. The waves are called magneto-hydrodynamical waves, in which the magnetic field acts on the ionized gas rather as though the gas were held together with elastic cords. In this theory, the waves are generated below the photosphere and pass out into the corona, where their energy is dissipated when the density becomes too low to support them. Qualitatively, this argument is plausible; quantitative answers are rather elusive, and the reason for a coronal temperature of a million degrees, rather than say 100,000° K, is unexplained. One interesting facet of the problem is that the corona finds it rather difficult to get rid of its energy, since it radiates very little light, and it cannot easily conduct heat down into the cooler photosphere. Outside the sun there is nowhere for it to conduct heat to at all. There must, however, be a balance sheet of energy gain and loss, and it appears likely that one of the most important losses is by the same radio radiation which tells us of the existence of this thin hot mantle of gas round the sun.

From the radio emissions of the solar corona, a useful picture of the electron density and temperature can be made out to distances of about three or four times the radius of the sun. The problem of corona heating would more easily be solved if these distances could be increased to ten or twenty radii, but no emission can be detected from the thin corona so far out from the sun. It would also be most interesting to plot the magnetic field of the sun to such great distances, as it is certain that this field is nothing like the field of an ordinary dipole bar magnet. Studies of the far-out corona are, however, not quite impossible, but they involve rather different radio techniques.

CHAPTER 4

The Corona Far Out from the Sun

THE corona, as it appears in the many photographs taken at times of solar eclipse, has one characteristic which is tantalizing above all others. This is its great extension, particularly in the equatorial streamers. It does not end in any abrupt way, nor does its density decrease very rapidly at the extreme limit of the photographable regions. What lies beyond, say, two million miles above the surface of the sun?

The problem is the more intriguing because we happen to live quite close to the sun, only 90 million miles away in fact, and as far as ordinary appearances go, we are not in the solar corona. But perhaps appearances are deceptive. The corona at its faintest, on eclipse photographs, has a density of about 10^5 electrons per cc., to be compared with about 10^{13} atoms per cc. in the high vacuum inside a radio valve. In the ionosphere a density of 10^6 electrons per cc. is found, falling off outside our atmosphere in an unknown way. Somewhere between the earth and the sun, there must be a minimum electron density, and here will be the boundary of the solar corona. At this boundary there must be some curious effects. The earth is rushing round its orbit round the sun at twenty miles per second, carrying its ionosphere with it. The solar corona will also be rotating with the sun, being tied to it by the sun's magnetic field; if the corona extends out to the earth's radius, the outer parts will be moving in the same direction as the earth, but overtaking it at about 250 miles per second – but perhaps this is all absurd, and the space between us and the sun is virtually empty. It is a rather difficult region to get at experimentally. We shall see in this chapter how far the approaches towards it from the directions both of the sun and of the earth have gone.

Zodiacal Light

In the early months of each year, there is a chance for anyone who lives away from the glare of the city lights to observe the zodiacal light. One must look into the western sky, about an hour after sunset, along the path which the sun took in the last few hours of daylight. Here one looks sideways on at the plane of the ecliptic, in which the planets revolve in their orbits round the sun, and here can be seen a faint wide streak of light, whose brightness fades away from the sun. This light comes from the sun, but we see it scattered from a mixture of dust and ionized gas lying in the plane of the zodiac. If we knew how much was dust and how much electrons, from the brightness of the zodiacal light we could find the density of the furthest-out portion of corona which can be directly observed. There is a good chance that this may be done, but better observations are needed, particularly observations that are not too much affected by the earth's atmosphere.

To reduce the effects of the earth's atmosphere it has been found necessary to observe the zodiacal light from great altitudes. Photographs of the night sky have been taken from aeroplanes and from mountain tops, using cameras with polarizing filters to sort out the light from the electrons, which is polarized, from that scattered by solid particles of dust, which is unpolarized. The latest measurements of the electronic component extend over 45° from the sun; it is this component that most interests the radio astronomer, as he can only observe ionized gas. Unfortunately the latest measurements cast some doubt on the separation of dust from electrons by polarization, and they can give no firm figures for the electron density.

The zodiacal light represents the limit of optical observations of the solar corona. At the equator a large extension of the corona is seen to extend out into the plane of the ecliptic. Near the polar regions of the sun optical observations are powerless to extend our knowledge beyond about two solar radii. We must rely on our radio eyes to find what goes on in the apparently empty space further out from the sun.

Radio Occultations

Radio emissions from the corona can give a good picture of the density and temperature out to a distance of about 3 solar radii. (The sun's radius is 700,000 km., or 450,000 miles.) Beyond that, the density is so low that any radio emissions would not be detected on earth. They would be of a very long wavelength, and would not reach us because of the blanketing effect of the iono-sphere.

Radio emission is, however, not the only way in which the corona shows itself to radio astronomers. It can refract and scatter radio waves, just as a turbulent cloud of hot air can disturb the view of objects beyond it. Hot air does not emit light, but it can refract it, and it can be seen by its effect on the visibility of distant objects, which become blurred and distorted as eddies of hot air cross the field of view. Layers of warm air over sunlit sands, road surfaces, or over the sea in calm conditions can so refract light that things appear to be in quite the wrong places, ships appearing to be in the sky, and the sky appearing on the road or desert surface as if reflected in pools of water. The corona is a region where the refractive index for radio waves can be sig-nificantly less than unity, which is its value in free space. Where it is zero, radio waves can be generated; where it is not zero, but is varying and slowly approaching unity as the distance from the sun increases, a bending of radio waves should take place.

Figure 6 shows the effect of this on a radio wave of about 4

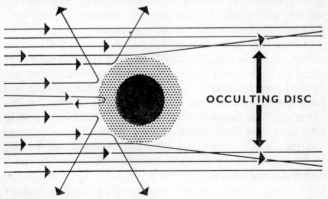

6. Bending of 80 Mc/s radio waves by solar corona. The occulting disc, through which radio waves cannot pass directly, is much longer than the visible sun

metres wavelength. The sun may be seen to present a disc of diameter about three times the visible disc as an impassable barrier for these long radio waves. At lower frequencies this occulting disc is even larger. A radio star which happened to be behind this disc would be completely cut off, and its radiation (as seen from the earth) would disappear. It would not be detectable again until the motion of the sun carried the corona several degrees across the sky, so that the radio star might disappear for as long as three days if it happened to be exactly on the track of the centre of the sun, in its path round the plane of the ecliptic.

It so happens that one of the brightest of radio stars, the Crab Nebula in Taurus, lies very close to the plane of the ecliptic, so that in June of each year the sun passes within about $4\frac{1}{2}$ solar radii from the path of the radio waves travelling from the Crab nebula to our radio telescopes. In Cambridge, in June 1950 and again in 1951, several instruments were set to watch this radio star day by day, with the hope that its radio waves would disappear behind the furthest parts of the solar corona, on or around 14 June. Nothing but frustration came from the experiments of these two summers, as the sun was so active that on every day in the middle of June intense sunspot radiation swamped the receiver, completely masking any effects on the Crab nebula. This was also the experience of Russian radio astronomers, who were quite independently trying out the same idea.

In June 1952 the experiment was repeated successfully – with greater success, indeed, than could have been expected. Instead of losing the Crab nebula for one or two days as expected, and that on the lowest frequencies only, it was found that the Crab was being affected by the corona for over a week, on all three frequencies in use. This meant that the corona was observable out to 10 solar radii. The observations of the occultation were all made with the use of interferometer aerial systems, which are sensitive to the angular size of the radio source (see Chapter 18), and it turned out that what had been seen was not a regular refraction, but an irregular diffraction – in other words, a heat haze, and not a mirage (see Figure 7). The corona must contain irregular clouds of electrons, through which the small bright radio stars become diffuse sources of radio waves, not losing energy by absorption in

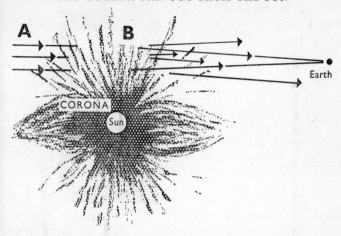

7. Diffraction in the solar corona. Parallel rays from a radio star (A) are scattered in the irregular corona (B) and are received over a considerable angle at the earth

the corona, but nevertheless recording lower values on the interferometers, because of their distorted shape. Figure 8 shows the results obtained in the first occultation of a radio star by the solar corona.

The success of this occultation experiment is to some degree a matter of luck. It is not easy to design aerials for use on wavelengths which have sufficient resolving power to distinguish between the radiation from the sun and that from the Crab nebula, when they are from the nature of the experiment so close together in the sky. In recent years A. Hewish, at Cambridge, has been able to use a large interferometer, designed for use on radio stars, but with the most convenient property of being able to remove the solar radiation almost entirely by its resolving power in a north-south direction. The records now obtained are not often seriously affected by sunspot radiation, and Hewish has been able to carry the study one stage further by looking at the occultation curve each year, through a large part of the sunspot cycle. In this way Hewish hopes to find out more about the shape of the corona,

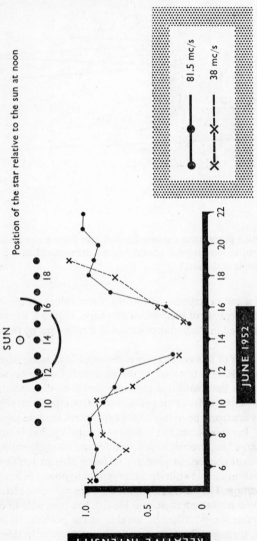

8. Occultation of a radio star by the solar corona

which is by no means spherical, and to determine whether it changes from year to year.

Results so far show that:

1. The corona at 15 solar radii ($3\frac{1}{2}$ degrees) contains irregularities of electron density of the order of 10^5 km. across, and of about 10^3 per cc. in density. It is quite possible that this density is the average density of the corona itself at this distance, so that the irregularities are in fact the whole of the corona.

2. These irregularities extend further out in the equatorial plane of the sun than they do in the polar direction. In the equatorial plane the corona has been traced right out to 80 solar radii.

3. Towards the poles of the sun, the electrons form into streamers that lie along the direction of the magnetic field, just like the polar streamers seen at a lower level of the solar corona in Plate 8B.

Scientists are never satisfied. If only we could have several occultations each year, we could carry on much faster with this exploration of the solar corona. At present it is only pursued during one rather busy fortnight each year, and it is anyway only a fortunate chance that the Crab Nebula is seen so near to the sun. It may be possible to use other radio stars in this way, but very much more sensitivity is needed and the chances of failure due to sunspot emission would be greater.

Whistlers

When a senior member of the radio group in the Cavendish Laboratory suggested that someone should do some research on whistlers, clicks, and the dawn chorus, no one at first took him seriously. But he had been studying reports of work at the Marconi Wireless Telegraph Co., in the days when telephone wires did not invariably pick up 50-cycle hum from power lines, and operators could listen to a silent wire, unaffected by background electrical noise from all kinds of electrical machinery. The reports were of strange noises, not man-made: whistles of varying pitch, clicks, tweaks, and other noises known only by various appropriately invented onomatopoeic names.

At this suggestion a remarkably simple experiment was carried out. An ordinary aerial, such as might be connected to a broadcast radio receiver, was connected instead to the input of an audio frequency amplifier, which is, in effect, the second half only of a radio set. A research student sat and listened to the output, and later began to record what he heard on a tape recorder. After some difficulty, he eliminated trouble from man-made interference, and made some most remarkable recordings. Everyone is familiar with the crashing noises of the 'atmospheric' picked up by a wireless receiver when lightning discharges nearby. This crash is also to be heard on the very-low-frequency radio waves picked up in the audio amplifier, but here it is often followed, at an interval of some seconds, by a whistle of falling pitch, somewhat like that of a falling bomb. Occasionally this is followed by a second whistle, and by others at regular intervals, all with a descending pitch.

The appearance was of some curious radiation from a lightning stroke, after it had completed its discharge, but whistlers still appeared on days when no lightning occurred in England, or anywhere nearby. O. Storey, who first unravelled the mystery, noticed that the whistlers which followed an 'atmospheric' had a mark distinguishing them from those that occurred independently. This was shown by a frequency analysis of the whistles, which were proved to fall in pitch at rates which divided into two groups, one approximately double the other. Those with double the rate of falling pitch were never associated with an 'atmospheric' and those with the lower rate usually closely followed an atmospheric.

The explanation followed from this clue. Storey was able to show that atmospherics from nearby lightning flashes not only induced an immediate impulsive signal in the receiver, but also launched a radio wave into the ionosphere, which travelled along one direction only, that of the magnetic field. The signal followed the lines of force like a tram on tramlines, bending back to the earth, and reaching it in South Africa. Here the radio waves bounced back, travelling along the same track, until they reached England again. They suffer a peculiar change on this long journey. The ionosphere exhibits the property of 'dispersion', which means that the speed of the waves depended on their frequency, so that the pulse was drawn out into a long oscillation, with the higher frequencies arriving first, and the lowest ones last. Successive reflections gave rise to a series of whistles, regularly spaced in time, and with a progressively greater dispersion of frequencies according to the total path travelled.

The whistlers with the least spread of frequencies, that is the fastest falling of pitch, and associated with no atmospheric disturbance here, were shown to be the result of a lightning discharge in South Africa, which had travelled to us, via the ionosphere,

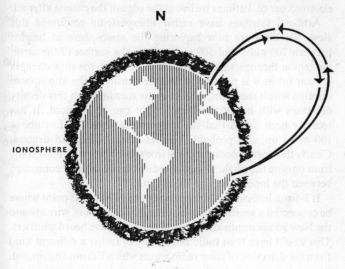

9. Path of whistlers. The radio waves generated by a lightning flash travel along the lines of magnetic field, far out beyond the ionosphere

along a magnetic line of force which virtually connects the countries together like a piece of wire.

The relevance of whistlers to the solar corona may be seen in Figure 9, which shows the location of the propagation path for a latitude about that of England. These paths reach out as far as 20,000 miles from the earth, far beyond the main part of the ionosphere. The path is, however, impassable, unless there are enough electrons all the way along it; the essence of the whistler results is that at a distance of 20,000 miles from the earth's surface there must still be at least 100 electrons per cc.

It is perhaps no coincidence that the best guess so far of the density of the solar corona as it falls off with distance, measured principally by radio methods, suggests that if the corona goes on decreasing at this rate all the way out from the sun to the earth, its density just outside the earth's ionosphere will be about 100 electrons per cc. Perhaps we live at the edge of the corona after all.

Artificial satellites have rather unexpectedly confirmed this view. Satellites are now exploring the atmosphere at heights between 100 miles and 500 miles above the surface of the earth, the region through which whistlers pass. From the slow changes in their orbits it is possible to find the density of the atmosphere through which they pass, and from the way in which this density decreases with height the temperature can be deduced. It has recently been found that the temperature rises very fast above 100 miles up, and probably reaches several thousand degrees. Clearly this energy does not come from down below: it must come from outside the earth. Here is another clue to a direct connexion between the ionosphere and the corona.

If Edison had carried his experiment of 1890 to the point where he connected a sensitive telephone to the long coil of wire around the New Jersey ironfield, he should certainly have heard whistlers. This would have been radio astronomy of rather a different kind from the detection of solar radio waves which Edison anticipated. The explanation of whistlers would have eluded him, for the ionosphere was quite unknown. It must be admitted that the explanation of the other strange noises, the clicks, and the dawn chorus, remain hidden from us in spite of our greater understanding of radio propagation. If they prove to be even half as interesting as the whistlers, they will be well worth investigating. A suggestion has already been made that they are sent out by an electrical impulse, not from lightning discharges, but from the impact of charged particles from the sun, striking the ionosphere at great heights. Our physical links with the sun are more tangible than is suggested by referring to those ninety million miles as the 'depths of empty space'.

That interesting boundary, where the atmosphere ends and the corona begins, must now be accounted as a real boundary on whose further side the gas moves with the rotation of the sun, and where, as Storey puts it, 'the interplanetary winds begin to blow'. Satellites do not reach this region, but lunar probes do, and they can find the boundary for us merely by recording the magnetic field. The earth's magnetic field cannot cross this boundary, and a space rocket will find a sharp drop in field as it rises past it. Advance reports from the first lunar probes suggest that the boundary lies at a distance of about ten times the radius of the earth.

CHAPTER 5

Sunspots and Flares

SIR EDWARD APPLETON occupies a very special place in the world of scientific radio. He was the first man to prove the existence of the ionosphere by demonstrating the reflection of radio waves, and the E-layer of the ionosphere, which he discovered, is often named after him. He has continued with ionosphere research for over thirty-five years since that famous discovery, and with his energetic exploration of many new lines of research it is not surprising to find him associated with the earliest observations in radio astronomy. Characteristically, his part was to realize the importance of a little publicized observation, and to demonstrate its physical significance.

The observations were of a strange sort of interference, experienced by radio amateurs experimenting with short-wavelength communications. The interference was of a subtle kind, since it gave very much the same effect as a deterioration in the performance of their receivers. Any radio receiver has a level of sensitivity below which it cannot receive signals, and this level is determined in good receivers by the electrical signals generated in the first valve amplifying stage. These signals sound like a hissing noise, and are called by radio engineers quite simply 'electrical noise'. No receiver is free from it; a deterioration in the performance of a radio communications link may well mean that the receiver has become unduly noisy. Jansky was very much concerned with just this noise in his original work in 1930 to 1932, although he was in fact recording the *extra* noise, of the very same character, that is received as radio signals from our galaxy.

The amateur work was done in the middle of the 1930s, several years after Jansky. The sky noise was found on occasion to increase to such a degree that the galactic signal itself was completely swamped, and even strong communication radio signals were lost in the extra noise. One can imagine the 'hams' of those days, checking every single stage of their equipment to track down this extra 'noise' and finally concluding that it must be just one of those awkward things that are sent to try us. But radio amateurs have always had a reputation for serious and painstaking research; they compared notes, collected times and intensities of signals, and looked for an explanation. Finally D. W. Heightman concluded that the extra noise was associated with solar activity. This conclusion explained the mysterious fact that Jansky had seen nothing of this trouble. For the sun was known to have a periodic change in activity through a cycle lasting about eleven years, and Jansky's experiment in 1931 had been at a time of minimum solar activity.

Appleton's attention was drawn to this phenomenon, but he was already being swept, as were many other radio scientists, into the feverish activity of developing Britain's new radar defence system. No further results were reported, the solar cycle waned, and the subject was dormant, and almost forgotten until it was dramatically awakened in 1942.

When the war started in 1939, a radar screen had already been constructed around our coasts, a screen which made possible the victory of the Battle of Britain. Many other radar devices were being developed which were later to play important parts in the war. Amongst these were the radar sets used to guide and control anti-aircraft guns, the gun laying, or G.L. radars. These sets were to be found all over England, sending radio pulses into the sky, with sensitive receivers waiting for the message that a returning echo would give. The direction and range of an enemy aircraft would then be obtained immediately, and the guns could go into action. Of course, the enemy knew about this, as we knew of his radar systems, and a grim game was played throughout the war of jamming or confusing one another's radar systems by various types of radio counter-measures.

To jam a radar system is easy. The enemy aircraft, wishing to avoid the accurate plotting possible on a radar system, transmits a powerful signal on the radar frequency, which swamps the receiver and makes the normal tracking system useless. But of course the receiver can still determine the direction of the aircraft from the direction of the jamming signal. A far more effective jammer would be one which could put a radar set out of action without the operator realizing that anything was happening. It is possible to do this by transmitting electrical noise, which will deceive the radar operator into thinking that his set performance is rather poor at that time.

Not all operators accepted this easy explanation, when on 26 February 1942 they found the noise level of their sets had practically hit the roof. They soon found the noise to be coming in through the aerials, not generated in the receiver itself, and many were able to give accurate 'fixes' on the source of the noise signals. At the Army Operational Research Group, Dr J. S. Hey collected all the reports together. His aim was to find out the location of the noise transmitter, and to find some way of preventing the G.L. radars from being put out of action every time the enemy turned it on. He very soon found that the 'enemy' in this case was common to both sides; it was in fact the sun. The German radar systems must have been subject to just the same mysterious type of jamming, but both countries would naturally keep their reports secret. Hey's findings were at first known only to the radar research establishments and to the services, but they were properly published when the war was over.

Appleton, who was now able to show that the noise which the amateurs had received on their sets came from the sun itself, which was radiating with fantastic strength at these times, made the first announcement. Later a joint paper, by Appleton and Hey, associated the strongest bursts of radiation with solar flares.

The quiet sun radiation at metre wavelengths is over a hundred times greater than that expected from a body like the visible sun at 6,000° K. This, as we have seen, arises because the sun is surrounded by an invisible corona at a temperature of about one million degrees. No such explanation could be given for this new enhanced radiation, as the intensity was of the order of a million times greater even than the quiet sun's signals. Later it was shown that only a small part of the sun's surface was now acting as a transmitter, and this area must have been so active that the idea of a temperature became almost meaningless.

The Origin of Sunspot Radiation

When the war ended, it again became possible for scientists to choose their own field of research, and several chose immediately to follow up the problem of this strange radiation from the sun. In Australia, a team under the head of Dr J. L. Pawsey, and in Cambridge a new section of the Cavendish Laboratory, under M. Ryle, both started to record solar radio emission on metre wavelengths, with apparatus of great sensitivity. They found that they were able to detect emission at all times, and started the earliest series of recordings of the daily levels of radiated power. They soon found that the power was very variable, with emission occurring sometimes for several days at a level some hundreds of times greater than that of the quiet sun. An outburst of this kind came to be known as a 'noise storm', and was found to be associated with visible sunspots. The largest increases were caused by solar flares, in which visible prominences are thrown out from the sun with incredible explosive violence. These outbursts were followed by the largest noise storms, and must have caused the noise interference to the earlier radio and radar observers.

In a full description of the behaviour of the sun it is usual to attempt a classification of the radio emission into various types. Classification is useful when it enables one to isolate and study a single phenomenon, but it is dangerous when it obscures relationships between different phenomena. We encounter this risk when we speak of 'sunspot radiation', meaning the very intense, very variable, circularly polarized radio waves in a noise storm.

The different types of solar radio emissions are in fact closely related, but their relation to optical phenomena makes the distinctions useful. The metre wavelength radiation, persisting for several days, at high levels, is distinguishable primarily by its association with sunspots. It is not such a close association, however, that one can look at the sun, count the spots, and predict the intensity of radio emission. The physical link between the visible spot and the radio waves comes through the most important single characteristic of a sunspot, its high magnetic field.

A visible sunspot is a dark region of the sun's surface of an area

61

which may easily equal that of Europe. It is dark because it is cooler than the ordinary photosphere, but it still emits enough light for the spectrograph to tell us about its temperature, and to show that the magnetic field is always high, often over 1,000 gauss. There is an ordinary magnetic field on the sun, rather like the earth's magnetic field. It is detected by its effect on the light from the sun, although it is normally seen only near the poles. Its strength is about 10 gauss, about five times the earth's field, but it seems that much larger fields must exist just under the photosphere at lower latitudes. These fields become distorted, and burst up through the surface, producing sunspots. They also produce radio emission which has the special characteristic of being circularly polarized.

Circular polarization can be thought of as radiation from electrons moving in a circular path, as for example round a magnetic field, as opposed to linearly polarized radiation from an electron oscillating in a straight line. The fact that the radiation is circularly polarized does not prove that it is generated in a region of

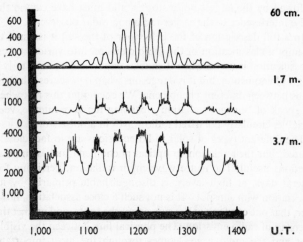

10. The active sun. Radiation from sunspots gives a large fluctuating signal on long wavelengths, and a slightly enhanced signal on 60 cm.

high magnetic field, for it is possible for such a region to filter out all but the circularly polarized component of radiation produced somewhere else, in a way which is similar to the way that polaroid glass acts on light. Whether the radiation is generated in a high magnetic field, or becomes circularly polarized by passing through one, it is certain that there is a high magnetic field at, or near, the point of origin.

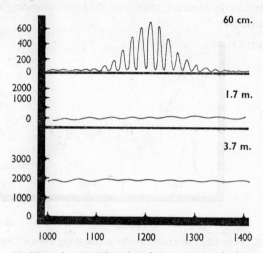

11. The quiet sun. These interferometer records show the sun to be more prominent against the Galactic background radiation at the shorter wavelengths. A steady signal from the sun gives the smooth sinusoidal variation as the sun passes through the interferometer lobes

Another characteristic of the sunspot radiation is a rapid fluctuation of intensity, giving 'bursts' which may double the intensity for about a second. The 'burstiness' is greater at longer wavelengths (Figure 10); at shorter wavelengths the sunspot radiation merges into the plage radiation mentioned in Chapter 3, which merely gives a smooth rise in the steady signal from the sun. Again, the duration of the bursts varies with wavelength, and a useful rule has been formulated, that burst length in seconds, times wavelength in metres, is approximately unity.

Some recordings of this type of radiation are shown in Figure 10. These records were made at Cambridge with an interferometer aerial, so that the sinusoidal variation of signal represents the passage of the sun through interference lobes of the aerial polar diagram (see Figure 3 on page 40). During the day, the intensity was substantially constant, apart from the bursts extending above the steady level.

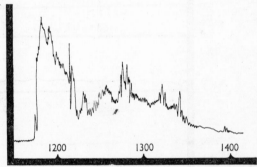

175 mc/s, 4 March 1947   G.M.T.

12. A recording of a radio outburst, occurring when a flare
was observed on the sun

Theories of sunspot radiation are not in a happy state. It is hard to see how electrons of quiet sun energies can radiate so strongly, unless they are organized, cooperating with one another by oscillating or gyrating in synchronism. Concerted action like this, encountered in radio transmitting aerials, is impossible in the sun, with no radio engineer to marshall the streams of electrons into organized paths. It appears more likely that electrons of very high energy are involved, each making a rather random but useful contribution to the total intensity. The details of the radiating process may be like those which govern the radio waves from the galaxy (Chapter 6). Whatever the precise explanation, no theory which does not involve both magnetic fields and electrons with exceptionally high energies has yet shown any hope of success. It all depends on the 'hot' electrons. The question is whether or not they exist, and here there is further evidence.

Cosmic Ray Bursts

While you read this page, at least one cosmic ray particle will probably pass right through you. This particle comes from cosmic rays which arrive at the earth from all directions, with a wide spread of energies, including some many times greater than any

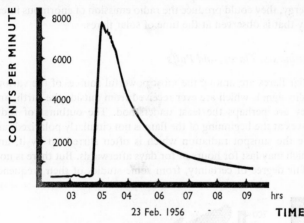

13. The sharp increase in cosmic rays observed at the time of a solar flare

attainable by electrical machines such as synchrotrons. Counts of cosmic rays usually show no variations with time, except changes that can be attributed to changes in the atmosphere. But occasionally the number of particles counted shoots up to large figures, sometimes more than double the normal rate, and this sudden increase may be noticeable for ten minutes or half an hour, dying down slowly after an initial sharp rise. The shape of the dying down curve, shown in Figure 13, is similar to the curves of many associated phenomena, and is the typical result of a large solar flare

There can be no doubt that these bursts of cosmic rays come from the sun. Somehow the intense activity of a flare, which is itself a very powerful electrical discharge, acts like an electric motor, and drives particles up to energies where their speed approaches the velocity of light. They then appear on earth at about the same time as light reaches us from the flare, and the cosmic ray counts increase. These particles may not be the actual electrons that radiate radio waves, but they tell us of the existence of high levels of energy, of about 10^9 electron volts, and if the electrons above a sunspot can attain a small fraction of this energy, they could produce the radio emission of enormous intensity that is observed at the time of solar flares.

Outbursts, Flares, and Puffs

Solar flares are among the most powerful sources of the various radio signals which are ever received from outside the earth, and they are perhaps the least understood. The outburst of radio waves at the beginning of the flare is not circularly polarized, unlike the sunspot radiation which is often stirred up by it, and which may last for hours or for days afterwards. But there is now a fair degree of certainty, from some studies of their frequency

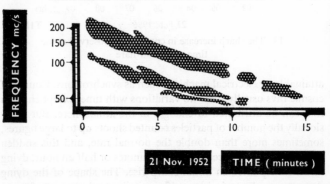

14. The dynamic spectrum of a radio outburst. This sketch shows the changing frequency structure of the first outburst to be recorded with a panoramic receiver

spectrum carried out by J. P. Wild, in Australia, about the place of origin of outbursts.

In Figure 14 a radio outburst is recorded on a receiver whose frequency is sweeping out a band from 40 Mc/s to 200 Mc/s and exploring the distribution of radio energy through that band. Such

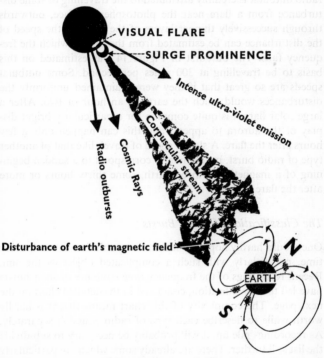

VISUAL FLARE

SURGE PROMINENCE

Intense ultra-violet emission

Corpuscular stream

Cosmic Rays

Radio outbursts

Disturbance of earth's magnetic field

EARTH

N

S

15. The effects of a solar flare

a receiver is called a 'panoramic' receiver. Following one frequency through, a sudden increase in intensity is seen at a definite time. But other frequencies start at different times, quite usually with high frequencies first and lower frequencies following. Now the solar corona at the time of a flare is an unknown quantity, but at any rate it probably is thinner at great heights than lower down. The lower the density, the lower the frequency of radio waves that might be generated. The analogy of an onion has already been given with reference to the quiet sun radiation, where successive skins correspond to successively higher frequencies as the heart of the onion is approached. The falling frequency of the radio outburst is credibly attributed to the travelling of some disturbance from a flare near the photosphere surface, outwards through successively thinner layers of the corona; the speed of the disturbance can be estimated from the rate at which the frequency falls. The outburst of Figure 14 was estimated on this basis to be travelling at 300 miles per second. Some outburst speeds are so great that if they were maintained uniformly the disturbances would reach the earth in an hour or two. After a large solar flare it is quite common for a particularly bright display of the aurora to appear, and this can happen only a few hours after the flare. A slower speed of travel, like that of another type of radio burst, may similarly correspond to a sudden beginning of a magnetic storm on earth, some thirty hours or more after the flare occurs.

The Classification of Radio Bursts

One would hardly hope for such an easy solution to work every time, particularly with such a complicated object as the sun. Recent recordings of the frequency time structure of solar bursts have led to a classification, contained in the detailed chart on the next page. The complexity of this chart means that it is hardly worth while to describe each type of radio emission separately. As recordings pile up, it will probably be necessary to sub-divide the list still further. There are already some which are particularly awkward to explain, as, for example, the type whose frequency variation is in the opposite direction, or where the direction may even change during the burst. A class of bursts worth particular notice is called the Type III burst; it sweeps through the frequency spectrum, from high to low frequencies, in only a few seconds, corresponding to velocities of about 30,000 miles per second. It is this type which goes with the bright flares, with aurorae, and with magnetic storms.

TYPES OF RADIO WAVES EMITTED BY THE SUN

(Based on a table prepared by Dr J. F. Denisse of Meudon Observatory)

Type of radio emission	Duration	Wavelength	Related optical phenomena	Radio polarization	Origin
Quiet sun	Continuous	All wave-lengths	Corona	Unpolarized	Thermal radiation
Radio 'con-densa-tions'	Several weeks	All wave-lengths	Calcium plages, or 'faculae'	Unpolarized	Local hot spots in the corona
'Micro-conden-sations'	Several weeks	Short wave-lengths	—	Partly circular	Uncertain
'R centres'	Hours or days	Long wave-lengths	Often above sunspots	Circular	Non-thermal 'sunspot' radiation
Type I burst	Ten or twenty seconds	Metre wave-lengths	Occur in the R centres	Circular	Unknown
Type II burst	Several minutes	Moving slowly through the whole spectrum	Small erup-tions, 'puffs'	Unpolarized	May be asso-ciated with the parti-cles caus-ing mag-netic storms
Type III burst	Several seconds	Moving rapidly through the whole spectrum	Large solar flare	Unpolarized	May be asso-ciated with cosmic ray particles
Type IV burst	Minutes or hours	'Noise storm'; on a wide range of wave-lengths	Following after a large flare	Circular	Unknown
U burst	Several seconds	Wavelength rapidly decreases and in-creases again	Often asso-ciated with flares	—	Similar to Type III

Light travels at a speed of 186,000 miles per second, and particles with high energies approach this speed the more closely as their energies are raised. The cosmic rays which come from the sun during Type III bursts move considerably faster than 30,000 miles per second, but it is nevertheless tempting to connect the two phenomena and to say that the cosmic rays generate the radio waves as they pass out through the corona.

It is rather gratifying to find that there is some optical evidence in favour of an ejection of material from a flare, just at the time when the radio burst starts. The flare has to be observed by the hydrogen light it emits, and it then appears as a bright area on the surface of the sun, near a sunspot. The less active bright marks are more persistent and fairly stable: they may be visible for many hours. Occasionally one of the more violent flares may be observed to blow off a sort of bubble, as a marsh will suddenly produce a bubble of gas. The bubble is pushed out and travels fast, up through the corona at just about the speed of the Type 3 radio outburst. The bubbles are rather nicely called 'puffs'.

Solar Terrestrial Relationships

Interest in the sun is natural when one regards it as our nearest star, one which is near enough for some considerable detail to be revealed with our radio as well as optical telescopes. There is however a very practical reason for studying the sun in all its phases of activity, since it is the prime controller of the ionosphere, and, via the ionosphere, of much of our radio communications. High frequencies may be propagated to embarrassingly large distances when the ionosphere is strong, and television sets in England may be jammed by police radio in Chicago or the radio control of a fire brigade in Spain. Medium frequencies, much relied upon for communication between ships, may suddenly be absorbed instead of reflected, and operators will blame their receivers rather than a solar flare.

Because of these close relationships between solar and terrestrial phenomena, it may safely be assumed that at any time several radio telescopes are steadily recording solar radiations, so that a complete watch is kept on the sun in the same way as visual observers watch and record visible sunspots and flares. Radio astronomy of the sun has only lasted just over one sunspot cycle, and the complex phenomena of radio emissions are hardly understood. We hope, nevertheless, that these remarkable manifestations of solar activity may prove to be useful in the urgent but difficult task of explaining and predicting the behaviour of the ionosphere. Their study may eventually provide information that will help in the maintenance of long-distance radio communication. But even if solar radio waves turn out to have no practical use whatever, they provide us with some of the most exciting and baffling puzzles that astronomers have ever had to tackle.

CHAPTER 6

The Galaxy

WHEN we turn our thoughts from the sun to the powerful radio waves which Jansky found to be radiated by the Milky Way, we are considering a region where distances pass outside the range of everyday understanding. Planets move round the solar system in times of less than a human life-span, and we can even fire rockets from the earth to form artificial planets. But the nearest stars outside the solar system are so far from us that even light takes several years to make the journey from there to the solar system, and light travels at 186,000 miles per second, as opposed to the speed of ten miles a second which may be reached by rockets.

The nearest stars show no particularly orderly grouping in the sky, but the further ones which are very much fainter and very much more numerous combine together to form the familiar bright streak of the Milky Way. This tight group of stars is surrounded at greater distances again by a vast emptiness, in which other blobs of light are to be seen, each containing thousands of millions of stars in a compact bunch. Each is called a galaxy, and our own is called the Galaxy, with a capital G. Our present understanding of the size and distance of these galaxies is of quite recent origin. Radio astronomy may prove very useful in studying the most distant of them, as we shall see later, but it has proved its worth above all in the study of our own Galaxy. The great penetration of radio waves allows the radio astronomer to explore the whole depth of the Milky Way, where most of the stars of the Galaxy are concentrated, and where a concentration of dust obscures light so severely that in some directions all but the nearest stars are blotted out. Furthermore, radio waves have been found to come from a great halo of space around the Galaxy, where no stars exist at all.

In Jansky's accounts of his early work on radio waves from the galaxy occur two rather speculative remarks on the origin of the radiation. Firstly, he suggested that the distribution of brightness over the sky agreed rather well with the familiar appearance of the Milky Way, so that the radio sources might be distributed in space in a disc, like the disc which contains most of the visible stars in the Galaxy. Secondly, from the character of the signals, which sound just like the hissing noise produced by thermal agitation in a hot resistor, he suggested that the origin might lie not in the visible stars, but in the tenuous ionized gas lying between the stars, a gas that might be kept hot by radiation from the stars. We shall see that Jansky's speculations fit modern observations remarkably well, although some surprising new features have come to light in the radio sky.

Before describing the appearance of the sky as we see it through a radio telescope, it is as well to recall the picture of the Galaxy given by optical studies. The stars which are outstandingly bright to the naked eye are near to the solar system in terms of the scale of distances we must use, being only tens or hundreds of light years distant. We must look at faint stars, thousands of light years away, before the structure of the Galaxy becomes apparent. And therein lies a great difficulty. The Galaxy also contains interstellar material in the form of dust, which obscures the view in the very directions in which we want to see the farther reaches of the galactic structure. In fact, the story of galactic structure must begin, not in our own galaxy which is partially hidden from us, but in other more clearly visible galaxies, the spiral nebulae, at distances from us a hundred times as great as the distance between our earth and the centre of our own Galaxy.

Pictures of extragalactic nebulae, such as those in Plates 1 and 2, are familiar to us today; it is surprising to find, however, that at the beginning of this century, even the rough shapes of these nebulae were hardly known. There was indeed only a suspicion that their distances were greater than most other visible objects. It was the work of Edwin Hubble at Mt Wilson Observatory, only about thirty to forty years ago, which established that these nebulae were composed of stars like the stars of our own Milky Way, and it was Hubble who first understood clearly that these were complete entities, floating isolated from one another by vast depths of empty space. He named them 'Island Universes'.

There are many different kinds of extra-galactic nebulae, and not all of them are spiral nebulae, but it happens that the nearest spiral to us is one which also bears a very close resemblance to our Galaxy. This is the Andromeda Nebula (Plate 1). Comparison with other nebulae shows that the oval shape is an effect of perspective, and that the nebula is shaped like a disc, in which lines radiate roughly spirally from a concentrated centre, tracing the regions where bright stars are to be found along with clouds of gas and dust.

In our Galaxy, the sun is embedded in a similar disc of stars and dust, and it lies in one of the spiral arms about two thirds of the distance from the centre. The bright stars we see around us are mostly in this arm, and consequently are to be seen in every direction. Only in the direction of the galactic plane are there very many distant stars to be seen, and here also the effects of dust obscuration can be seen as dark rifts in the bright background of the Milky Way. In the Andromeda Nebula, the dust is not so effective a screen, as it can at most cut off the light from the further half of each spiral arm in the nebula, leaving us a complete picture of one side.

Because the solar system is embedded in interstellar dust, hiding most of the distant stars, our own Galaxy has to be examined by less direct methods. A classical problem in dynamical astronomy has been to use the observed motion of the nearby stars, relative to the sun, to derive the distribution of mass in the Galaxy: the stars are moving round the disc in circular orbits, at speeds which depend on the mass inside their orbits. The velocities of stars are deduced, partly from their apparent motion across the skies, and partly from their radial velocities as measured by the Doppler shift of spectral lines. It has proved quite easy to find from these velocities the total amount of matter in the Galaxy, but it is on the other hand rather hard to provide more than a general law of the variation of density with radial distance from the galactic centre, even taking no account of the variations in thickness. This cannot take us very far in the examination of our own Galaxy, since at great distances many stars in the vital directions in the Galactic plane are obscured, and the movements of those that are visible are small and hard to measure. Nevertheless, a distribution of stars in the disc can be found by this method, and can be shown to resemble that of the Andromeda Nebula.

Again, the distances of stars can be measured by observing the intensity of their light, their optical 'magnitude'. Provided that allowance can be made for obscuration in the dust clouds, this depends only on the type of star and its distance from us. This technique applied to some particularly bright stars – the O and B stars found in the spiral arms of the extra galactic nebulae – provides some idea of the distribution of these kinds of stars in the disc. A definite indication of lanes of stars running tangentially to the radius of the galaxy can be found, just like the arms of a spiral galaxy.

The plane of a galaxy is not, however, the only place where stars are to be found. Some galaxies indeed, have little or no disc, and appear to consist of a spherical or elliptical blob of stars. An example can be seen in Plate 3B. Our Galaxy contains some types of stars which are found in a similarly widespread distribution, concentrated in the centre, but extending out in all directions from it. Clusters of stars, known as the globular clusters, are found at great distances from the galactic plane, and these do not contain the bright hot stars to be found in the spiral arms. The widespread halo, or corona, of stars, appears to be quite distinct from the plane both in shape and in population.

Astronomers have long classified stars into types, designated by initials, forming the sequence, O, B, A, F, G, K, M, R, N, S (traditional mnemonic: Oh! Be a fine girl, kiss me right now. Smack!), in which temperature decreases progressively from O to S. The O and B stars are those which are hot enough to heat the interstellar gas all round them, and produce the H II regions (Chapter 7), which are found in the spiral arms. Other members of this main sequence of star types are also found in spiral arms, but they are rather less concentrated to the plane. A very different population of stars is to be found in the widespread halo of the galaxy, and this clear cut distinction is now recognized in the designation Population Type I for the disc, and Population Type II for the halo.

The optical appearance of our Galaxy from outside must then be somewhat as suggested in Figure 16, which shows a rough

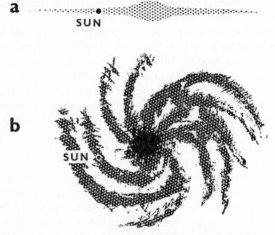

16. Sketch of the Galaxy (*a*) from the plane of the Galaxy, (*b*) from above

spiral structure, with the sun in one arm, and a Type II population of stars distributed thinly throughout a roughly spherical halo, concentrated on the centre of the Galaxy. About one hundred thousand million stars make up the whole Galaxy, with most of them lying fairly close to the Galactic plane.

Radio Surveys of the Galaxy

The appearance of our Galaxy, in terms of radio waves rather than light radiations, has now been outlined by a series of experiments in radio astronomy. Jansky found that a part of the background radiation comes from the plane of our Galaxy, but radiation is also received from all other directions, and it is not obvious at first sight that much of this also comes from the Galaxy. The radio astronomer's way of sorting out the mass of seemingly meaningless signals received is to make maps of the sky in terms of radio waves, at several different frequencies, and to try to compare the distribution of radio brightness with that of optical brightness.

Making maps of radio brightness is easy in principle. A highly directive aerial array must be scanned over the sky, and the recordings made of the variation of received power can then be used to make a contour map. But the two fundamental difficulties of the radio astronomer, sensitivity and resolving power, make the realization of this no easy task. We will leave the description of the radio telescopes which are used for such surveys until Chapter 18, but some idea of the limitations must be given, so that the present results can be appreciated. The shortest wavelength at which the background radio waves are bright enough for maps to be of some value over the whole sky is at present about 1 metre. Maps are required at wavelengths up to 10 metres, but even at one metre it requires an aerial of the size of the Jodrell Bank radio telescope to produce a beam width of 1°. Smaller instruments will have larger beams, and consequently are unable to discern small details in the sky. Parts of the sky have been mapped at a wavelength of 3·7 metres, with a resolution of 1°, by the Mills Cross aerial in Australia, and most of the Northern sky has been covered by an aperture synthesis aerial in Cambridge, at 8 metres, with a beam of about $\frac{1}{2}$° by 3°. These two aerials, which will be discussed further in Chapter 20, have proved that good resolution is possible at long wavelengths, but at present we are limited, for complete and accurate maps, to a few surveys with rather larger beamwidths. One of these is shown in Figure 17.

These maps reveal immediately that most of the background radiation comes from our own galaxy. Firstly, they all show the Milky Way as a prominent feature, running along the centre of the maps. (The coordinates of the maps measure distances along the plane of the Milky Way and perpendicular to it, a system which gives a map similar to a Mercator Projection of the terrestrial globe.) Secondly, the brightness falls away steadily from the equator, although it is by no means negligible in directions perpendicular to the equator. The way the contour lines tend to run parallel to the equator shows that the main structure in the background radiation is related to the structure of the Galaxy. Whether or not all the radiation comes from the Galaxy is another question: in fact, since many discrete sources of radiation are known outside the Galaxy, it is certain that there must be an extra-

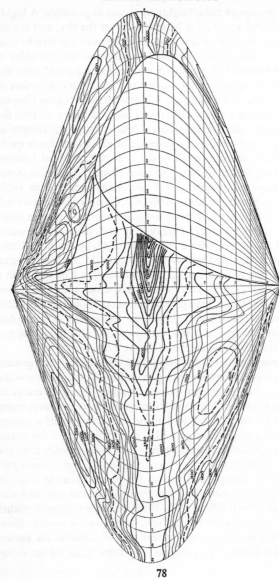

17. The radio sky at a wavelength of 3·7 metres. The plane of the Galaxy lies along the equator. The blank area is the part of the sky not seen from Cambridge

galactic component, which would be expected to be roughly uniform over the whole sky. We have not only to find the distribution of emission through the Galaxy: we have also to find the amount of this extra-galactic component.

Analysis of the map made at 3·7-metres wavelength has shown that the extra galactic component is very small. Just how small it is, is a question which must be answered later, in the investigation into the nature of the radio stars, but for the moment it may be neglected. The rest of the radiation comes from the Galactic plane, both from sources very close to the plane, and from some spread-

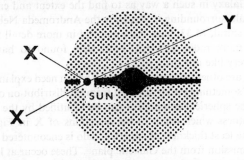

18. Halo round the Galaxy. From the sun the maximum halo radiation is seen towards Y, and the minimum towards X

ing out from it as do the visible stars. A further and unexpected part comes from a sphere which encloses the whole Galaxy like a halo (Figure 18). The sources along the plane fit well with the visible star population Type I, but the sphere is far more extensive than the Type II population of stars, as it extends in all directions out to the maximum radius of the disc. The radiation from this spherical halo is generated fairly uniformly throughout the sphere, whereas Type II stars are concentrated strongly towards the centre of the Galaxy. The outer parts of the sphere seem to extend into empty intergalactic space, and it is quite certain that there is no type of visible body distributed in this way. The radio waves are generated in an invisible halo.

The inference of the existence of a spherical halo round our Galaxy, is not, of course, a unique conclusion from the evidence provided by the contours of radio brightness. No indication of the distance from which the radio waves have come is available. An infinite number of solutions must therefore exist to the problem of turning the two-dimensional map into the three-dimensional model, but it is reasonable to choose only distributions which are symmetrical about the centre of the Galaxy, provided of course that they fit the observations. Further, our Galaxy is not the only one to have a halo, and in fact it was a published radio map of the Andromeda Nebula that first led Shklovsky to postulate the existence of haloes, and later led J. E. Baldwin to analyse the radio map of our Galaxy in such a way as to find the extent and emissivity of the halo surrounding it. Recently the Andromeda Nebula and another spiral, M 33, have been mapped in more detail with the Jodrell Bank radio telescope; both were found to have large haloes very like our own.

There are other features on the maps which need explanation in terms of something rather different from the distribution of visible stars. The spherical component can be identified by the minima of brightness which occur in the directions of X in Figure 18, where the least thickness of spherical halo is encountered with no added emission from the Galactic plane. These occur at latitudes of $\pm 45°$ on the map. The main extra component, apart from the plane, is the bright strip which runs from near the galactic centre right up across the sky, at right angles to the plane, and over near the galactic pole to meet a fainter strip near the anticentre. This belt of radiation probably extends round the whole sky, although the southern part of the sky is not covered by the same surveys. We shall call this feature quite simply 'The Belt'. There are other less prominent features, notably one at $l = 270°$, $b = 50°$, which has been associated by some authors with a cloud of extra galactic nebulae in this direction. It is rather more likely, however, that this is another feature of our own Galaxy, although no such explanation of it has been clearly justified.

The Origin of Galactic Radio Waves – Synchrotron Radiation

For the origin of the radio waves from the Galactic halo and from the Belt, one might look to the hot gas between the stars, but in fact there proves to be no easy solution here. The temperature of the interstellar gas is known to be much less than 100,000° K, which is the temperature required to explain the radio intensity at long wavelengths. Nor does the variation of intensity with wavelength accord with the spectrum of thermal radiation from a hot gas. (See Chapter 7.) The explanation that has now gained wide acceptance was first made as a hypothesis to explain cosmic radio waves as radiation from the denser atmospheres of radio stars, rather than the diffuse interstellar gas, but Russian theoreticians were later able to demonstrate its application to Galactic radiation. The mechanism is called synchrotron radiation, or Schwinger radiation, after the man who first described it.

Schwinger himself was not concerned with radio waves, or indeed with astronomy; he was interested in the behaviour of electrons inside electrical machines for accelerating nuclear particles to high energies. In one of these machines, a synchrotron, electrons are whirled round a circular track to which they are confined by a very strong magnetic field. At very high energies, the electron beam emits a blue glow of light called synchrotron radiation. Schwinger showed that this radiation was a natural consequence of the acceleration of electrons in a strong magnetic field, and showed that the energy lost in radiation was an important factor in the design of accelerating machines. The acceleration causing the radiation was of course there whether or not the electrons were increasing speed: in fact their speed was so near to that of light that only a very small increase would ever be possible. Any particle constrained to move in a curved path is accelerating, and the acceleration increases in proportion to the curvature imposed upon it.

Analysis of the rate of synchrotron radiation from an electron shows that it varies with both the electron energy and the strength of the magnetic field which bends its path. Magnetic fields in synchrotrons are of the order of 10,000 gauss: in interstellar gas we may expect only 10^{-5} or 10^{-6} gauss, that is, from ten to one millionths of a gauss. Nevertheless the distances through which we look in the Galaxy are so great that a very small concentration of electrons with high energies could account for the total radiation in the halo.

Shklovsky and other Russian authors have made a detailed analysis of the relation of the observable radio waves to the electrons and magnetic field causing them. It has been found that the spectrum of the radio waves can be used as a measure of the energy spectrum of the electrons, that is of the proportions of electrons with various energies. All the energies involved are of the range encountered in the proton cosmic rays which reach the earth. It is now generally supposed that the electrons are generated by the protons, and form another way in which cosmic rays may be observed: we are in fact extending our knowledge of cosmic rays beyond the limits of the techniques which record directly the arrival of particles on earth. The relation between radio spectrum and energy spectrum is close, on account of the rather limited band of frequencies radiated by an electron of a given energy, so that the intensity of radiation at any frequency is a measure of the number of electrons which have a corresponding energy.

The simplest mathematical description of these spectra, in the form of a power law, fits quite well the proton cosmic rays and the radio wave spectrum. It follows that a power law fits also the electron energy spectrum: if we write this in the form $N = KE^{-m}$ (where $-m$ is called the spectral index), showing that the number N with energy E falls off with the mth power of the energy, then the radio spectral index will be $-\dfrac{m+1}{2}$. This means that the experimental determination of the radio spectral index will provide a direct measure of the relative population of cosmic ray electrons with different energies.

The Spectrum of the Radio Sky

The background of radio radiation comes largely from one source, the galactic halo, and it follows that a determination of the spectrum of the galactic halo emission can be made with quite simple aerials, as no close angular discrimination is needed. Near the plane of the galaxy, some difficulties arise from the H II emission, to be considered later, but otherwise the variation in brightness with frequency can be measured by connecting a series of similar aerials to accurately calibrated receivers on different frequencies. The results of one such experiment are shown in Figure 19, where the brightness temperature is seen to vary as the sky sweeps across the aerial beam in one day. Three frequencies were used, and the scales of the resulting graphs were adjusted so that they would fit over one another. Except near the galactic plane, the fit was found to be very good, with temperatures following the law temperature proportional to frequency to the

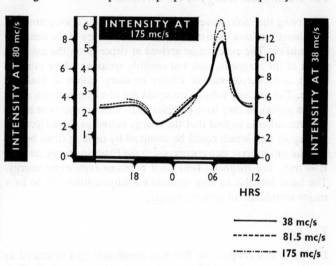

19. Variations in brightness temperature as the sky sweeps across aerial beam in twenty-four hours. Recordings on wavelengths of 38, 81·5, and 175 Mc/s

power −2·5. The differences near the galactic plane are to be attributed to the H II regions; the remainder of the sky now appears as one large and homogeneous source of radio waves.

The very satisfactory result is now obtained that throughout the whole galaxy the electrons are spread in energy by one and the same law. To a good approximation the number of electrons with a given energy is proportional to the value of their energy to the power −1, which is about the value one would have guessed from the observed cosmic ray particles. It should in fact be possible to go further, and find how the primary cosmic rays are related to the electrons. For example, the electrons could be generated in collisions of the protons with dust particles or atomic nuclei; a theoretical examination of this process might be expected to give the exact law of electron energies that has now been observed.

The Density and Energy of the Electrons

Observing the radio waves from the Galaxy over a wide range of wavelengths allows us to calculate the total energy of the electrons responsible. The exact value arrived at depends on the assumed value of the magnetic field, but roughly speaking, there must be about one electron-volt of energy in every gallon of Galactic space. The average volume occupied per electron is much more than a gallon, as they have energies of 10^9 electron-volts or more. It is remarkable to find that the energy stored in these electrons is roughly that which could be obtained by turning three bodies like the sun entirely into energy, using the Einstein energy relation $E = mc^2$. The magnetic field itself contains even more energy. The halo, invisible to conventional telescopes, turns out to be a major storehouse of galactic energy.

The Belt

Earlier in this chapter the Belt was mentioned, and described as another feature for which there is no optical counterpart. The Belt deserves further discussion, however, as it has other interesting features; in fact its invisibility optically may result from the simple fact that it is not a real object, but a kind of radio illusion.

Our evidence for the existence of the Belt lies in the bright streak seen in the map of Figure 17, lying across the sky perpendicular to the galactic plane, and crossing it near the centre of the galaxy. Its origin must lie in the Galaxy, for it is impossible to conceive of such a bright patch occurring in the almost uniform background of extra galactic nebulae which surrounds our Galaxy; furthermore, its situation and shape connect it immediately with galactic structure. Economy in hypothesis demands that we try to see if synchrotron radiation could by any simple means produce the Belt from radiating electrons which are invisible optically. There is only one Belt in the whole Galaxy, and we are in the centre of it. Just as Galileo found it impossible to believe that the Earth is at the centre of the universe, so we must find it at least improbable that the Earth is near the centre of the only ring in the Galaxy.

Is the Belt then a kind of mirage? Is it perhaps a rainbow, or halo, an appearance only, dependent on being seen from a particular direction?

The theory of synchrotron radiation enables us to say that this could indeed be so. The spiral arms of the Galaxy contain magnetic fields of rather greater strength than the halo, and their fields may exceed 10^{-5} gauss. More important, these fields are aligned along the arms; not exactly, perhaps, but with lines of force roughly lined up like the separate fibres in a single strand of wool. Fast-moving electrons will move in spirals around the local spiral arm, undergoing a considerable acceleration at right angles to the arm. Their synchrotron radiation is consequently to be found only in a very narrow range of angles at right angles to the magnetic field; it is only the rather irregular nature of the magnetic field that broadens this narrow angle into a belt several degrees across. A perfectly smooth field would make the belt into a thin bright streak in a perfect circle across the sky.

A rainbow is a rather personal affair. Its end is in a different place for everyone. If we move, it moves with us. In a similar way, the Belt is now seen to be rather personally attached to our Solar System; a bright streak to be seen by us, but not by the inhabitants of another planet in another solar system far removed from our own. They, of course, may have their own Belt, invisible to us. Perhaps they have radio astronomers too, puzzling about their own Belt. But if they are familiar with sunshine and rain, and have advanced beyond feeling themselves to be unique in a boundless universe, they are likely to draw the same comparison between their Belt and their own rainbow.

From the large-scale structure of the Galaxy, we now turn to the fine details to be seen right in the plane, where the hot O and B stars are to be found, and where the spiral arms are the most prominent feature.

CHAPTER 7

Hot Hydrogen

IT is small wonder that the gas between the stars is hard to detect optically, as it is so tenuous as to constitute a far better vacuum than any we can create on earth. If from the best possible vacuum that we can obtain, we take away all but one in a thousand million of the remaining particles, we have something resembling the emptiness of interstellar space. Nevertheless, there can be found among these few scattered particles many different types, among which only a small proportion are the cosmic ray protons and electrons with which the last chapter was concerned. Visually the greatest impact of the interstellar medium is by the obscuration by dust of the light from distant objects, but there are places where a tenuous gas may be seen either radiating or reflecting light from a neighbouring star. Hydrogen atoms are the most important constituent of gas clouds, and, in general, when a cloud is hot, it emits the red light characteristic of hot hydrogen gas, and it is then known as an H II region. H II is the name given by spectroscopists to an excited, or ionized, hydrogen atom. Cooler, unionized, hydrogen, called H I, lies in clouds which emit no light at all, although as we shall see later it does have its own special form of radio radiation.

By the photographic device of comparing photographs of the same region of the sky, taken with plates sensitive to red and to blue light, it is possible to make the bright H II clouds of gas quite conspicuous. The whole sky has recently been covered by photographs taken in this way with the 48-inch Schmidt telescope on Mt Palomar.

An H II region may be complicated affair, like the Orion nebula shown in Plate 5, or it may be rather simpler, and more compact, like the Trifid nebula in Plate 6B. A feature which all the H II regions have in common is that they all contain at least one very hot star of the so-called 'early' types O and B. The nebula in Orion owes its complexity to the large number of these stars; another well-known H II region, the Rosette nebula, has four

exciting stars in a compact group, and provides us with a straightforward picture of a roughly spherical region, with well-defined
boundaries, containing a fairly constant density of hot hydrogen;
the temperature may be found spectroscopically, and, in round
figures, it is 10,000° K – rather hotter than the surface of the sun,
but not as hot as the surface of the O and B stars, some of which
reach a temperature of 40,000° K. It may seem strange to assign a
temperature of 10,000° K to a region of nearly perfect vacuum,
but the temperature is not so much the temperature of space as of
the few atoms that are there. The speed of these atoms determines
their energy, and their energy determines their temperature.

The astrophysical problem raised by the H II regions is not to
explain these very high temperatures, as these follow from the
close proximity to a hot star, in every case, but to seek an explanation for their formation in such well-defined clouds. The H II
cloud is not the only form of interstellar gas. It is in fact merely
the part of the interstellar gas which is hot, and it is surrounded
by cooler, unionized gas. Ultra-violet light from the central star is
continually flowing through the H II region, ionizing and heating,
and energy is correspondingly flowing out from the H II region as
it radiates light and radio waves. The balance is sharpened by a
kind of safety valve, which opens when the temperature reaches
10,000° K, and radiates energy away very much faster than can
the hydrogen alone. The 'safety valve' is oxygen, present in small
proportions, which radiates strongly only when the temperature is
high enough for it to be ionized. It then radiates, producing its
characteristic green line in the spectrum, until the temperature is
down to about 10,000° K. The temperature is kept constant in this
way over the whole region where the ultra-violet light is potent.
The radius of the ionized sphere will depend on the type of
star exciting it, and its density will vary, according to the density
of the surrounding gas, but the temperature of each H II region
remains fairly well fixed.

Radio Waves from Hot Hydrogen

Any hot body emits radio waves, with an upper limit of intensity determined only by its temperature. It may emit less than

this maximum if it is shiny or transparent. The same radiation rules apply as for heat and light, and we may again appeal to an analogy to help our understanding of the radio emission from H II regions. Apart from its temperature, the solar corona is rather like an H II region, so that we can use the same analogy as in Chapter 3.

If for the H II region we substitute a glass sphere, heated to a dull red heat, say at a temperature of 500° C, just below the melting point of glass, how much heat and light will the sphere give? The answer will depend on the surface condition of the sphere; whether it is silvered or smoked black, for example, and, if the surface is clear, the answer will depend on the transparency of the glass. A blackened surface emits the most radiation and a shiny one the least. If the glass is completely transparent, then nothing at all can be seen of its radiation. If it is opaque it radiates as though it were black. If it is partly obscuring, the radiation will depend on the thickness of the glass, increasing with thickness until the glass is effectively opaque, at which thickness it will give the full 'black body' radiation. Black body radiation varies with frequency according to a well-known law, which, for radio waves, says quite simply that the intensity of the radiation varies as the frequency squared. This is often referred to as a 'spectral index of plus two'.

The H II region emitting radio waves is subject to the same radiation laws as the glass sphere emitting heat and light waves, but a special feature of the H II regions makes the application of these laws more complicated and more interesting in this part of the spectrum.

It so happens that most H II regions are, in the radio range of frequencies, just on the border of opacity. Above a certain frequency, usually about 100 Mc/s, their opacity falls off as the square of the frequency, while below this frequency they become rapidly opaque and give only the black body radiation. The ideal radio spectrum resulting from this behaviour shows a transition from a spectral index of two to an index of zero as frequency increases past 100 Mc/s.

The frequency of transition is that at which the region is just completely opaque, or rather, at which the total absorption becomes a calculable amount. This frequency is a measure of the square of the electron density multiplied by the depth of the nebula.

The spectral curve of a simple H II region therefore gives, in quite a direct way, a measure of the electron density of the interstellar gas. As the measured quantity is exactly the same as that already known from optical measurements, the usefulness of such a radio astronomy method might be questioned. But the real value of the radio measurements is in the indication they give of the presence of extra radiation, above the thermal radiation, from some nebulae that might otherwise have been considered as normal H II regions. For example the nebula known as IC 443, shown in Plate 7B, does emit the hydrogen lines optically, but radio measurements show that it is very far from being an ordinary H II region, as it has too intense a radiation and quite the wrong spectrum.

The Orion Nebula

The Orion nebula is a more complicated object than the idealized H II region considered so far. Nevertheless it is a nebula which radiates thermal radio waves; and it is an object which is visible with the naked eye. With the aid of field glasses or a low-power telescope it is possible to distinguish that this star, the highest one in Orion's sword, is in fact a nebula, appearing as a small cloud rather than the distinct point of a single star. It is well worth looking at, as it is in fact a kind of stellar maternity home, a crucible of hot gas where stars are born. There are many hot young stars in the Orion nebula, and there is a pair of stars known as AE Aurigae and μ Columbae streaming away from the centre of the nebula in diametrically opposite directions, with extremely high velocity. These stars are twins, born together but rushing away from each other at the rate of 150 miles per second. The main mass of the nebula is, however, in the form of dust and gas (Plate 5).

The whole region of the Orion complex is about 5° across, constituting a rough sphere, with a bright edge (Barnard's Ring). The Orion nebula is the brightest object in this region, and is itself a complicated H II region, excited by a large number of hot stars, perhaps as many as 70.

Orion has a very dense central region, surrounded by a more diffuse outer part, and the combination of these curved spectra gives a variation on the simple spectrum. There is apparently no extra, non-thermal emission from the nebula, or indeed from Barnard's Ring or any other part of this complex of stars and ionized gas.

Radio astronomy has acquired a reputation for providing startling discoveries about every celestial object which provides detectable radio waves. H II regions provide a salutory exception, where such a close correspondence between optical and radio observations has been found that the radio measurements could all have been inferred from the measurements made at a wavelength about one million times as short. Incidentally, this provides a nice correspondence between processes which are essentially quantum physics (the emission of light waves from excited atoms), and a process which is essentially classical (the emission of radio waves from accelerated electrons).

It is not often that radio physics is concerned with quantum processes at all, but in the next chapter we see that for unionized hydrogen, the H I atoms, quantum physics plays a direct part in the generation of radio waves from the Galactic plane. This unionized hydrogen is the same gas that makes the H II regions, but it is far away from the influence of starlight, and it is cold and lifeless. No less attractive region of the universe can be imagined, but from no other field of radio astronomy have such detailed results been derived.

CHAPTER 8

The Hydrogen Line

THE growth of radio astronomy has been rapid and spectacular. Its history is for this reason well known in many details, each separate branch immediately calling to mind the names of a few individuals who provided the impetus to a new field of research. Of these individuals the name of H. Van de Hulst especially deserves mention, partly as his contribution was made in unusual circumstances, but more particularly because it was the first which came as a result of theoretical rather than experimental work.

During the years of the German occupation of Holland, the Leiden Observatory was, as it is now, directed by Professor Oort. But there was little work to direct in a practical field, and Professor Oort was mainly concerned to keep discussions and theoretical work alive amongst the few students who had escaped detention. Among these was Van de Hulst. The idea of using radio waves to extend the study of the universe was discussed several times, but Professor Oort maintained that radio was a very weak and blunt astronomical tool compared with the optical spectroscope. How could distances, velocities, and temperatures be measured unless a spectral line could be observed? So he set Van de Hulst the task of finding, by theory alone, if any of the common constituents of interstellar space might be found to radiate a spectral line in the radio range of wavelengths.

Spectral lines are emitted by a discrete quantum process, in atoms or molecules. The energy of the emitter can only assume certain levels, and a change from one level to the other, involving a change of energy E, is accompanied by the emission or absorption of energy at a frequency ν, where $E = h\nu$, and h is Planck's constant. For visible spectral lines the change E is of the order of five electron volts, or about 10^{-11} ergs, so that for radio waves, where the frequencies are about 10^6 less than light waves, the energy change must be only 10^{-17} ergs. The problem then is to find an atom or molecule which not only has two energy levels

91

only 10^{-17} ergs apart, but which could be expected to exist at these levels when the element was found in the cold spaces between the stars. Van de Hulst was able to show that the unionized hydrogen atom, called by spectroscopists the H I atom, had a pair of energy levels separated by this amount. The 'ground state', or lowest energy level, in which a hydrogen atom would normally be found in interstellar space, was in fact split into two levels by a magnetic coupling between the proton nucleus and the single electron. A close analogy is obtained by considering both proton and electron as weak magnets, constrained to lie parallel to one another and magnetized either in the same direction (parallel) or in opposite directions (anti-parallel). The parallel situation has a very small excess of energy over the anti-parallel situation; one can picture the magnets flipping over to the anti-parallel case, using up stored energy in doing so.

Having found the energy levels, the next stage is to determine the probability of a transition occurring from one level to another. It turns out to be an unlikely occurrence – left to itself, an excited, or parallel atom would flip over and emit its quantum of radio energy only after some millions of years. In the Galactic plane the emission is stimulated by collisions with other atoms; even this only decreases the life-time of an excited atom to fifty years. But there are very many hydrogen atoms in the disc of the galaxy, and Van de Hulst was able to show that even this small transition probability gave a fair chance that the hydrogen line would be detected.

Not long after the war, as part of an independent atomic physics research programme, physicists in the U.S.A. showed that it is possible to stimulate the transition in a beam of hydrogen atoms, and thereby to measure the radio frequency of the spectral line. This was measured, with great precision, as 1,420·403 Mc/s, giving a wavelength of just over 21 cm. (The wavelength of sodium light, for comparison, is about 6×10^{-5} cm.)

At the end of the war Leiden Observatory was able to publish this new idea, and to start experiments to detect the 21-cm. spectral line in galactic radiation. These experiments met great technical difficulties, which culminated in a frustrating conflagration in which the whole receiver was destroyed. The credit for the first detection of the line went instead to Harold Ewen, then a research student at Harvard. Publication only came when his results had been disclosed to Leiden, and to the Australian observers, Christiansen and Hindman, who with commendable speed managed to improvise equipment and confirm the result within two months of the first discovery.

We must now see how the more detailed measurements now being carried out enable us to map out the hydrogen throughout the galactic plane, with its temperature, density, and velocity directly available from the spectral line.

The Temperature of Interstellar Hydrogen

Near a hot star, the hydrogen is ionized, and is at a temperature of 10,000° K. Far away from stars, there is nothing to keep the gas hot, and its temperature falls to about 100° K (that is −173° C); it may even be colder than this in places. The temperature of these H I hydrogen atoms can be deduced from the intensity of the spectral line, just as the temperature of the H II regions can be deduced from the intensity of radiation from the ionized hydrogen atoms they contain. Using again the analogy of a transparent sphere, again the determining factor is the transparency of the material. For H I the opacity is simply calculated from the total number of atoms in the line of sight, and if this is sufficiently large a cloud of unionized hydrogen will radiate the 21-cm. line with an intensity exactly corresponding to its temperature. If the opacity is small, it is found that the intensity is simply proportional to the number of atoms in the line of sight. We may therefore measure in some directions a temperature, in others a density, and in others a combination of the two. A map of the sky is therefore rather like a contour map in which two quantities are represented at once by the same contour lines. Sorting out these two quantities will need some further clues and perhaps some guesswork. Furthermore, even though the contours contain information about the temperature and density, the map remains a two-dimensional map of a three-dimensional galaxy. A simple analogy – with obvious limitations – will illustrate the difficulty.

Suppose that from a secure position somewhere within a swarm of bees, one is trying to map the shape of the swarm. In all directions the view is of bees, but in some directions there may be more bees visible and in other directions fewer. It might be possible to measure and map the total number of the bees in any line of sight, but what would this tell us of the shape of the swarm? We must know something about their distances before the whole three-dimensional picture can become clear.

Among bees, this knowledge of the distance of any particular part of the swarm might be denied to us; but in mapping our galaxy, the spectral line measurements give us precisely this information. We can in fact produce a map of the distribution of hydrogen in the galaxy that is really three-dimensional. Some discussion of the Doppler effect in the hydrogen line will be necessary to explain how this can be done, for it is the Doppler effect that gives the spectral line measurements this overwhelming advantage.

The Doppler Effect in the Hydrogen Line

In these days when aeroplanes fly at speeds approaching that of sound, the Doppler effect is all too familiar to us. Sound waves from rapidly moving sources are compressed as the source approaches, giving a sound of shorter wavelength and higher frequency; as the source recedes the wavelength is increased and the pitch falls. When an aeroplane passes at very high speed, the fall in frequency of its engine noise may be so great as to leave the observer with only a faint rumble of sound. In the most distant parts of the universe, where galaxies are receding from us at speeds comparable to the speed of light, the light will similarly be changed very greatly in wavelength, but at the much lower speeds encountered in the Galaxy a simple law applies: the apparent frequency of the source differs from the true frequency (ν) by an amount ($\Delta\nu$) proportional to its velocity ν, so that:

$$\frac{\Delta\nu}{\nu} = \frac{\nu}{c}$$

where c is the velocity of light.

The Doppler effect is, of course, well known in optical spectral lines, where it can be used to measure the radial velocities of stars: in the 21-cm. radio spectral line, it is a particularly powerful tool, since the frequency shifts can be measured directly with an accuracy of a few kilocycles per second. Using the Doppler law, we find that one cycle in a frequency of 1,420 megacycles is equivalent to $v = \dfrac{1}{1420,000,000} \times 3 \times 10^{10}$ cm./sec., i.e. to about 20 centimetres per second, or about $\frac{1}{2}$ m.p.h., so that the change

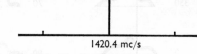

1420.4 mc/s

(a) Diagram of ideal hydrogen spectrum

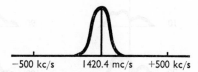

−500 kc/s 1420.4 mc/s +500 kc/s

(b) The spectrum is widened by the random motions within a hydrogen cloud

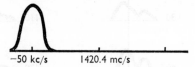

−50 kc/s 1420.4 mc/s

(c) The cloud as a whole is receding with a velocity of 100 km/s

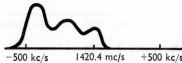

−500 kc/s 1420.4 mc/s +500 kc/s

(d) In general the profile is complex owing to clouds at various distances each having their own velocities

20. The profile of the spectral line emitted by interstellar hydrogen at a frequency of 1,420 Mc/s (wavelength 21 cm.)

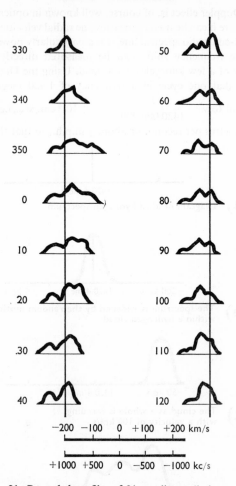

21. Recorded profiles of 21-cm. line radiation from hydrogen at various longitudes in the Galactic Plane (from the work of Leiden Observatory)

in frequency of a hydrogen-line radio transmitter carried by a pedestrian could easily be measured. Velocities in the Galaxy are commonly some thousands of miles per hour.

In any direction in the galactic plane we look out through a disc containing a series of spiral arms radiating out from a central concentration of stars. It has been known for some time that this

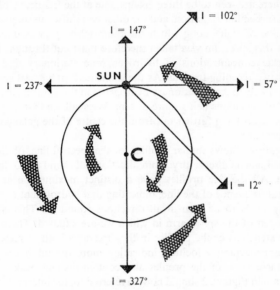

22. Diagram for interpretation of hydrogen-line profiles. C is the centre of the Galactic plane. Inside the circle through the sun the rotation appears to be clockwise, and outside this circle it appears to be anticlockwise

disc is rotating, and, further, that is does not rotate as a solid disc, but with a motion like that of our solar system, where each planet pursues a course round the sun with a velocity depending on its distance from the sun. The result is that a line of sight in the galactic plane must contain parts of the plane which appear to move towards or away from us, and this movement will cause the spectral line of the hydrogen, in this direction, to show a corresponding spread in frequency. Given the law of galactic rotation, any frequency component of this spread line can be directly related to a definite point in the galactic plane.

Take for example the spectral line shown in (d) of Figure 20. This is an actual example of the H I spectrum from a direction in the galactic plane. All the deflections come from H I radio waves, but there are seen to be three groups, one at the frequency of the undisturbed line radiation, and the other two shifted in frequency. The line of sight along which the radio telescope was directed when this spectrum was taken therefore must cut through three separate concentrations of hydrogen, one stationary and the other two receding from us. As the sun is itself in a spiral arm, it seems likely that the stationary hydrogen is in this same local arm, the moving clouds being more distant. We shall see that they are in two arms lying further out from the centre of the galaxy than the local arm.

Figure 21 shows similar profiles for the spectral line, obtained by the Leiden Observatory, from directions all round the Galactic plane. All the line profiles have a distinct maximum near the natural frequency of the line, indicating that hydrogen at rest, or nearly so, is to be seen in all directions round us. This is the hydrogen of the spiral arm in which we are situated. There are also extensions of the profiles in the directions both of receding and approaching velocities, indicating more distant hydrogen, and these parts of the profiles also contain distinct peaks. The diagram in Figure 22 should now be referred to, for interpretation of these profiles.

In this diagram the rotation of the disc of the galaxy has been reduced by about one revolution in two hundred million years, so that the sun appears no longer to be moving round the centre. The inner parts of the galaxy are now rotating clockwise, and the outer parts are rotating anticlockwise. The directions marked correspond to the coordinates in the set of line profiles, and are known as the galactic longitudes. We are now able to interpret the line profiles in a representative selection of directions, labelled by their galactic longitudes.

(i) Longitude 330° (in Sagittarius). This is near the direction of the centre of the Galaxy. Here, the circular motions are all perpendicular to the line of sight, and no large Doppler shifts are observed. The line profile is centred on the frequency radiated by stationary gas.

(ii) Longitude 120°. This is not far from the anticentre direction, where again all radiation is at the centre frequency.

(iii) Longitude 100°. The line of sight velocity is here towards the observer and increases with distance. Two spiral arms are crossed here, each giving a separate component to the line profile.

(iv) Longitude 60° (in Cygnus). Looking tangentially one sees first the local spiral arm end on, giving a large zero velocity component, and after it traces of the outer spiral arms, each at its own shifted frequency.

(v) Longitude 10°. A line in this direction includes both approaching and receding parts of the plane. The maximum velocity of recession occurs when the line is nearest to the centre, and a fairly sharp cut-off on the low-frequency side of the line profile shows this clearly, giving incidentally a value for the velocity at this point. Beyond the circle, on the sketch, approaching velocities are again observed, but at such distances that only small signals are received.

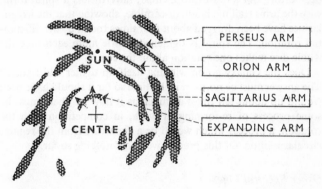

23. Spiral arms in the Galaxy. This sketch map of the hydrogen concentration in the plane of the Galaxy shows three spiral arms near the sun. Towards the centre of the Galaxy the map is incomplete, but the position of an arm which is expanding outwards is known

With this identification of Doppler shift with distance as a key, the profiles can now be interpreted into a map of the hydrogen in the galactic plane. For first approximation it need only be a two dimensional map, since the hydrogen is mostly found within about 300 light-years of the plane, while the extent of the plane is more than 40,000 light-years across. Such a map is found in Figure 23, where the major concentrations of hydrogen are shaded in. Two series of observations, from Leiden and from Sydney, are combined for this map, since no single observatory can see and map the whole sky.

The Spiral Structure of the Galaxy

The map in Figure 24 has the obvious defect of not showing us a neat and tidy series of spiral arms, radiating uniformly from the centre of the Galaxy, but a glance at other spiral nebulae, Andromeda for example (Plate 1) or M81 (Plate 2), shows that this is hardly to be expected. The appearance is more of a whirlpool, in which each part of the surface moves in a circle, twisting the ripples into a spiral form. In the Galaxy the irregularities have been drawn out almost into a circle; nevertheless a spiral form, with the arms trailing, is still discernible, showing that the irregularities have been dragged about four times round by the differential rotation. The spiral is tightened a little more each time the whole disc makes one rotation about the centre.

Does the Galaxy go on winding itself up tighter and tighter? The answer must be no, as in its lifetime so far it should have been wound up about ten times as much as it now is. There must be some process of re-forming at work, in competition with the rotation, a process which would be a departure from the regular circular motion. Of this process we know nothing so far.

Other Spectral Lines

Are there any other spectral lines at radio frequencies, and would they help us in any way to understand the Galaxy? There must indeed be very many possible lines; some have become familiar to us by their use in atomic clocks, such as the ammonia and caesium clocks. But the radio frequency resonances in molecules of ammonia or caesium are of no interest in astronomy if there are no such molecules in the interstellar gas, or again if they are there but not excited into emitting a radio wave. Yet again, the energy transition which would give the radio wave may be even more unlikely to occur than the 21-cm. transition in hydrogen. All in all, the chances of observing any other lines are very slim.

One line, however, has been looked for very carefully. Deuterium, the heavy form of hydrogen, is known to exist on earth at about one four-thousandth the concentration of normal hydrogen. The question of its concentration in other parts of the universe is one that cosmologists would greatly like to have answered, as it involves the question of the origin of all elements heavier than hydrogen. The deuterium line has a wavelength of 92 cm., or a frequency of 327 Mc/s, and it might be seen most clearly by its effect in absorbing radio waves from a particularly strong source at the very centre of the Galaxy which is known to radiate all observable frequencies. No one has in fact recorded the presence of deuterium so far, although attempts have been made both in Russia and in England to record absorption at this frequency of the radio waves from the galactic centre.

Galactic Structure – a Summary

There is, of course, a great deal of simplification in the outline of Galactic structure revealed by the various types of radio waves discussed in the last three chapters, and indeed there must be oversimplification at any point of contact between an astronomer and the universe. In one sense this is justified, for how can he begin to understand and know individually the hundred thousand million stars in our Galaxy, or indeed the untold millions of galaxies in the universe? He must sort and classify, starting with the simplest and broadest divisions, and trying always to bring order and understanding to the finer and smaller divisions to which he is driven.

We see our Galaxy optically at present as constructed in two main parts: the Type II population stars accounting for most of both the bulk and the mass of the Galaxy, and the Type I population accounting for the most spectacular parts, the spiral arm structure. But sub-division can go on almost indefinitely within each main population, a complication redeemed by recent work showing that stars do evolve from one type to another. Radio astronomy is far from such detail. The galactic halo of radio emission is somewhat like the Type II population, but does not follow the same mass distribution. Very little detail is known about its outer edge, for example, or about changes of density within it. Radio emission from nearer the galactic plane, though not in the plane itself, does follow the mass distribution of the Type II stars rather more closely, but we are not yet in a position to classify this as a separate radio 'population'.

There remains the distinct spiral arm or Type I population. Here it does seem that the radio emission bears a very close relation to the visible stars. In a spiral arm, dust, stars, and gas, ionized and unionized, exist together. Here is the birthplace of stars, where the tenuous gas of hydrogen is shrinking into condensations. In regions like the Orion region, some condensations become so dense that their gravitational field attracts further gas to themselves, and stars are formed. These are the early type stars, Types O and B, which become very hot and eventually produce enough radiation to ionize the gas around them, forming an H II region.

The radio emission comes from both the cold primal hydrogen gas, as the 21-cm. line emission, and the hot clouds surrounding the newly-formed stars within the arms. Radio astronomy brings to our knowledge of the Galaxy a picture not so much of the stars, but of the gas between them, outlined by that basic building unit of universes, the hydrogen atom.

CHAPTER 9

Supernovae

ON 11 July 1954, a gathering of radio astronomers met in Cambridge to celebrate a birthday. This was no ordinary birthday party: it was the 900th anniversary of the birth of a new nebula.

In the ancient records of the Chinese astronomers appear several accounts of the appearance of bright new stars in the sky. For example:

2nd cyclical day, 5th month, 1st year of Chih-ho of Sung, guest star appearing at South East of T'ien-kuan several ts'un long, lasting more than one year

and again:

60th cyclical day, 10th month, 2nd year of Chung-p'ing of later Han, guest star appearing at Nan-mên, big as half a mat, five colours and different tempers, later a little diminishing, disappearing in the 6th month, next year.

The first of these refers to the year A.D. 1054, a classic date for astronomy. It is possible, from this quaint account, to find quite accurately the time and place of one of the most dramatic events that man can hope to see – the supernova explosion of a star. No star was actually born at this time, but a star which was already old was suddenly transformed into one of the brightest objects in the sky. The star had been shining steadily, obtaining its energy from the conversion of hydrogen into helium, a controlled and orderly version of the hydrogen bomb. In the process it had been shrinking and becoming hotter inside. A core of helium was collecting, an apparently inert ash from the nuclear burning of hydrogen. But the temperature continued to rise until a critical level was reached, when helium itself began to release energy by combining to form nuclei of larger atomic weight. The succession of nuclear fusion continued through carbon right up to iron, until energy was released so fast that the whole massive core of the star exploded with the violence of a colossal thermonuclear bomb.

The star was blown apart, as a glowing sphere of gas, leaving behind only an insignificant remnant. This sphere of gas is still to be seen with a telescope of moderate power, still expanding and glowing with light nine hundred years after the explosion; it is known as the Crab Nebula in the constellation of Taurus (Plate 7A). It is the first in the list of nebulae compiled by Messier in 1784, and it is often referred to as the nebula M1. It is the only clearly recognizable remains of a supernova explosion, and as such it has been closely studied. It is fortunate that so much light is still emitted from the nebula so that we are able to observe it in great detail.

A radio astronomer who particularly should have been at the party is John Bolton, as it was he who made the discovery from the Sydney Radiophysics Laboratory in 1947 that the Crab Nebula is a very powerful radio transmitter, nearly the strongest in the Galaxy. At that time radio astronomy consisted of a rapidly growing study of solar radio waves, together with the old observations by Jansky and Reber of the background of cosmic radio noise. Bolton tried a new idea, and began to look for individual discrete sources in this background. The results of this search are another story, except that one of the first 'radio stars' to appear in his records turned out to be in the constellation of Taurus, and near enough to the Crab nebula for a suspicion, almost a certainty, that 'the Crab' was the source of the radiation he had detected.

There have been other supernova explosions. The Danish astronomer Tycho Brahe, known for his accurate observations of the positions and movements of planets, and Kepler, the interpreter of these observations in terms of elliptical orbits, recorded the positions of bright new stars which for a time completely dominated the sky. Both of these men worked before the invention of the telescope, but nevertheless their positions are reliable to about one minute of arc. Very little is to be seen in these positions now, except for traces of wisps of gas, still blowing away. And even these were found only recently, with the help of the 200-inch Palomar telescope. We cannot find out very much about these supernovae, as compared with the Crab nebula. Even their distance is uncertain, whereas the distance of the Crab nebula is

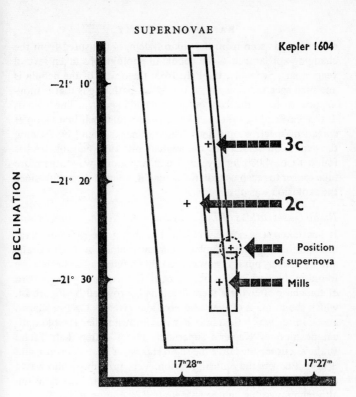

SUPERNOVAE

Kepler 1604

−21° 10′

−21° 20′

−21° 30′

DECLINATION

3c

2c

Position
of supernova

Mills

17ʰ28ᵐ   17ʰ27ᵐ

RIGHT ASCENSION 1950.0

24. Supernova positions. The map shows the measured
positions of the radio stars believed to be remnants of the
supernova observed by Kepler. The rectangular areas show
the accuracy of the observations

known with greater certainty than that of most astronomical
objects. In terms of galactic distances they are probably fairly
local, and are to be found in, or near, the same spiral arm of our
galaxy as our own solar system, but partly hidden from us by the
obscuration of dust clouds.

The distance of the Crab is found by observing its actual rate
of expansion in two separate ways. Firstly, the angular rate of

expansion, as seen from the solar system, is measured from the changing appearance of the nebula in photographs taken several years apart. Secondly, the light from the centre of the nebula is analysed spectroscopically; it originates both in gas that is moving towards us at the front of the shell and in gas receding from us at the rear, and this range of velocities reveals itself in a Doppler spread of spectroscopic lines. The distance is found by dividing the expansion velocity by the angular rate of expansion, and is found to be 4,000 light-years. Light and radio waves therefore take longer to reach us than the actual life span of the nebula since the explosion was observed.

Radio Observations of Tycho Brahe's and Kepler's Supernovae

It has taken a great deal of effort to bring the radio observations to the degree of angular accuracy attained by Tycho Brahe and by Kepler, but it is now certain that a faint radio star is to be found in the positions of both supernovae. An interesting record of the chase after these identifications is provided by Figure 24, which shows maps of the radio positions given as lozenge shaped areas, inside which the radio star was known to lie. The old optical position of Kepler's supernova agrees better than Tycho Brahe's, but for the latter the radio star has a large diameter, and it in fact covers the optical position. Very probably radio waves are coming from a large nebula made by the supernova explosion, although no visible light is now emitted from most of this nebula.

Radio Observations of the Crab Nebula

This nebula has been a source of great joy to optical and radio astronomers alike. It is within the range of present radio telescopes to measure its radio emission using wavelengths from 1 cm. to 10 metres, and its spectrum is found to be in a class of its own. The distribution of brightness across its surface has been found first by interferometers, and, later, by watching the emission reduce steadily as the moon's disc crossed the nebula in a dramatic radio occultation. But the nebula became the focal point of theories of radio emission because of a characteristic common to its light and to its radio waves, which is most unusual in both. Its light and its radio waves are linearly polarized.

The synchrotron radiation has been discussed at some length in Chapter 6, as the source of radiation from the galactic halo. In fact the first suggestion that this mechanism might operate in the radio universe was made by two Swedish physicists, Alfven and Herlofson, who proposed it not for the galactic halo but for radio stars. The Russian development of the idea eventually brought out the idea that the radio waves from the Crab nebula, and indeed most of the light as well, could only be explained by synchrotron radiation. No other mechanism could produce so much light from the gas of one supernova. Furthermore, both the light and the radio waves should be plane polarized, a very easily detectable condition.

Photographs were immediately taken in Russia of the nebula, using polaroid set at various angles across the telescope, and at once a considerable polarization was found. A beautiful set of photographs made later at Mount Palomar reveal that every part of the nebula is emitting light which is completely plane polarized, although the combination of the light from separate parts with different directions of polarization obscures this complete polarization in some parts.

Here, at last, was proof of the only plausible hypothesis, and at the same time a challenge to radio astronomers to find a similar polarization in the Crab's radio emission. The radio astronomer, without the fine resolving power which produced the photograph of Plate 7A, can expect to find only a small effect, say 10 per cent polarization, for the combined radiation of the whole nebula. Further, the Faraday effect of the rotation of the plane of polarization as a wave traverses an ionized medium with a magnetic field tends to confuse the polarization still more. Nevertheless, radio polarization has been detected by American observers, using 3-cm. wavelength. The Faraday effect gives the least trouble at short wavelengths, so that their figure of 7 per cent polarization probably represents the largest effect to be found anywhere in the radio spectrum. Certainly at metre wavelengths, the measured polarization is less than 1 per cent.

Detection of radio polarization is, in principle, a very simple matter. A dipole aerial, working either by itself or in the centre of a parabolic reflector, responds only to one plane of polarization. If it is slowly rotated about the direction of the radio waves, it will measure in turn all possible planes of polarization, and a signal varying as it turns will reveal the degree and direction of the polarization of the radio waves. The aerial which is used must be rather carefully constructed so that no variations occur except from genuine polarization. The work on the 3-cm. radiation was done at the Naval Research Laboratory in Washington, using a parabolic reflector fifty feet in diameter which has a very accurately machined surface of solid aluminium.

Confirmation of the radio polarization of the Crab Nebula has now been secured by Russian radio astronomers.

Other Supernovae

The dates at which supernovae have been observed in the Galaxy are the years A.D. 1054, 1572, and 1604. This series, it must be admitted, provides no reliable guide as to the frequency of occurrence of supernovae, as it has been followed by a blank period of 350 years. Supernovae can, however, be seen in other galaxies, and a fair guess at their frequency of occurrence in a spiral galaxy of our type indicates that one might be seen every few hundred years on the average. There will be others which will explode in our own Galaxy without being seen from this planet. A supernova occurring in the Galactic plane, unless it were very near to us, would be hidden by the dust which is concentrated in the plane. In fact, for every one seen, it is possible that as many as ten may occur unseen, and out of these there must be some which now are radio stars. To search for these we must look for radio stars near the Galactic plane, and then look for optical or photographic evidence of any remains of an explosion near them. Among such radio sources is one of the brightest radio stars in the sky, Cassiopeia A; and in the position of this star we find a most remarkable nebula.

The Radio Star Cassiopeia A

In 1948 at Cambridge, an interferometer was built for the study of the Cygnus A star, already reported by Hey and by Bolton.

The first record obtained showed that Cygnus A was outshone by another radio star, which was too far north in the sky to be visible to Bolton in Australia and out of reach of Hey's aerial which looked only at the horizon. A rough position was soon found, but no obvious identification was possible.

As a research student in the Cambridge team the author was given the task of finding an accurate position of this new radio star. The main objective was to try and identify this important source of radio waves with a visible star or nebula. A special interferometer was built, using two 27-foot parabolic reflectors from old German radar sets, and was operated at a frequency of 214 Mc/s. During a long series of observations, three other radio stars were also measured, among them the Crab Nebula, whose identification was already fairly certain. The position of Cassiopeia A was eventually found, to an accuracy of ten seconds of arc in Right Ascension, and forty seconds in Declination (these are the positional coordinates for celestial objects, corresponding to longitude and latitude for terrestrial positions), and the position was passed on to the Cambridge observatories. With the optical instruments available Dr David Dewhirst was able to show that there was a very faint nebula near to the radio star position, and Baade and Minkowski at Mt Palomar were therefore asked to take the optical comparison to its limits by checking the position with the 200-in. telescope. The photograph of Plate 8A is the result of their cooperation in this piece of detective work.

One might expect the brightest radio star to be an outstanding visible object, but Cassiopeia A is certainly not this. In fact it is possible to miss it entirely at a first glance at the photograph, until one is given the clue that the nebula occupies almost the whole of the Plate. Near to the top of the photograph is a large blob of nebular gas, which is in fact the piece found by Dewhirst, and over an area of about 5 minutes of arc in diameter, there are more clouds and wisps of gas that are in fact all that can be seen of a sphere of hot gas.

In spite of the faintness of the nebula, Dr Minkowski managed to obtain spectra of several of the filaments of gas, and found that the nebula had some optical characteristics which placed it quite out of the ordinary, and indeed matched its radio performance.

He found two kinds of filaments, one nearly stationary, and the other moving at speeds of around 5,000 km./sec. (about two hundred thousand miles per minute). These move so fast that their detailed appearance changes appreciably in only a few months, and photographs at intervals of two years show some distorted almost out of recognition. No other massive body moves so fast in the whole of our Galaxy. Further, the gas in the filaments is very hot. There are oxygen and neon atoms there which have been stripped of four electrons by the thermal agitation. A highly energetic, ionized, fast-moving gas is just the place for the generation of radio waves, and we can be fairly sure that there is a magnetic field as well, giving the conditions necessary for synchrotron radiation.

What then is this nebula? The first attempt to make sense of the motions of the filaments and to show that they were all streaming out from one place, as they would in a supernova, failed in this, and showed only a complicated, almost turbulent action. There was a spirited argument for a while, until, after some years, the motions could be followed more clearly from a succession of photographs. Then it became obvious that the fast-moving filaments were all flowing out fairly regularly after all, but that the others were part of a more chaotic system. The slow filaments also had a quite different spectrum, and it seems that they may be clouds formed when fast filaments collide with cold interstellar matter, and fall behind the rest of the explosion shell.

From the speed of the movements of the fragments, the explosion of Cassiopeia A as a supernova could be dated to about A.D. 1702, within a few years. Its distance is 10,000 light years, and this, placing it well away from our own position in the Galaxy, could explain why it was not seen and recorded as a supernova along with those of A.D. 1054, 1572, and 1604. It appears to have been a rather different and more powerful type of supernova explosion than the other three, but at a distance of 10,000 light years it might only have reached 5th magnitude, which is only just visible to the naked eye.

There must, of course, be others like it, although no other in our Galaxy is quite as powerful. Cassiopeia A, placed at the most distant part of the galactic plane, would still be a very prominent radio star, brighter than any others that have been found in the Galaxy.

Another identified radio star is the nebula known as IC 443, from its position in the Index Catalogue of Nebulae (Plate 7B). This beautiful object is much less energetic, both as a radio transmitter and in optical appearance; nevertheless it is hard to believe that such a well-defined and symmetrical cloud could have come from anything other than a supernova. It may be that the explosion was less violent or that it occurred in a region of high density gas which has blanketed and slowed down the expanding shell. More likely it is very much older than Cassiopeia A, and has spent most of its energy. Radio waves do not come uniformly from the whole of this nebula. There is a bright filament near the centre, which is an especially powerful patch; perhaps this has not yet lost so much of the explosive force of the supernova.

We cannot tell how many of these remains there are in our galaxy, but they are certainly not uncommon, and some of them are certainly young. The concept of an unchanging universe implies little change over periods of at least a million years, but in our galaxy we apparently have nebulae as young as a few hundreds of years old, and another could be born tomorrow, without warning. Nothing could please astronomers more! The heavens as they are, are exciting enough, but the birth of a new supernova in our Galaxy would be headline news all over the world. Every telescope would be trained upon it, and photographic plates and films used at a rate at least as great as that expended on a new Hollywood star. Radio astronomers would compete to be the first to detect any build up of radio emission, and then would follow its rise as the hot sphere of gas grows, generating its own magnetic field, and giving a spectrum of radio waves which, one hopes, would reveal some of the complex dynamics of such an energetic cloud.

The stir created by the Russian launching of Sputnik I would seem trivial in the face of such excitement, and no doubt journalists and astronomers alike would cheerfully lose sleep, as then, in the cause of its observation. But however much we may wish for a supernova to appear in our own lifetime, these things are outside our control and for the moment we content ourselves with watching Cassiopeia A. The visible parts of this are moving fast; does the radio source also expand?

There have been some good measurements of the apparent size of the radio source, and by combining results from Cambridge, Jodrell Bank, and Nançay in France, a fair description of the general shape of the radio nebula has now been obtained. At Jodrell Bank there is now a record of one dimension of the nebula, to an accuracy of a few per cent. In a few years' time a repetition of this observation should show if the radio and light sources are expanding together. The total intensity of the radio emission seems to be falling by about $\frac{1}{2}$ per cent each year; a repetition of the diameter measurements should soon show whether the radio and light sources are expanding together. No other radio star can be expected to show any appreciable change, in size or in brightness, during our lifetime. The heavens are not unchanging, but they cannot be said to change very fast.

Some details of the known supernova radio sources are given in the Table on page 131. Radio astronomy has provided a great stimulus to the study of supernovae, and it has trebled the number of them known. The total of nine includes only six clearly visible nebulae, three of which were observed as exploding stars and three as older nebular remains. The last three of the nine are more speculative, as they are classified mostly on radio data alone. But for dust obscuration in the Milky Way, it is likely that several more would be added to the list. As things stand at present, it appears that the nature of many radio sources in the Milky Way will never be certainly discovered.

CHAPTER 10

Extragalactic Nebulae

ONE of the greatest astronomers of recent years was Edwin Hubble, whose devotion to the problem of distant nebulae was combined with the most fruitful use first of the 100-in telescope on Mt Wilson, and later of the 200-in. telescope on Mt Palomar. The distant nebulae were often described in astronomical works of the beginning of this century, but their actual distances were then dismissed merely as 'large'. Sir Robert Ball, for example, in *The Story of the Heavens* (1894) gives the spiral nebulae only a very brief mention in comparison with other topics, and says:

It is believed that some of these nebulae are sunk in space to such an appalling distance that the light takes centuries to reach the earth.

Hubble grasped the true situation. Hundreds of light-years may seem an appalling distance, but his new distances were many times beyond those of any Galactic objects, and quite beyond any description by mere adjectives.

The 100-in. telescope was completed soon after the end of the First World War, and during the 1920s Hubble revolutionized our concept of the universe by demonstrating the aggregation of stars into galaxies, and by showing that our Galaxy was only one of innumerable 'island universes' which were so distant as to appear as small diffuse nebulae. In the constellation of Andromeda there is one such nebula which can be seen by the naked eye. Hubble was able to show that this nebula was a great star system like our own Galaxy, at a distance from us of about two million light years. The diameter of our galaxy is less than a tenth of this distance.

The 200-in. telescope was first used in December 1947, although it was not until eighteen months later that all tests and adjustments were complete. It had taken twenty years to build; no less than eleven of these years were occupied in grinding the concave face of the mirror. The aspirations and dreams of one man,

George Ellery Hale, who inspired the whole programme of construction of the 60-in. and 100-in. telescopes on Mount Wilson, have now produced a beautiful scientific instrument, satisfying to look at and deeply rewarding to use.

With this instrument, nebulae of the Andromeda type can be detected to a distance of about 1,000 million light years, and in this distance there must be well over 100 million galaxies. Eddington, in his book *The Expanding Universe*, gave the following multiplication table, which is still the best guess we have at the statistics of the universe:

$$10^{11} \text{ stars} = \text{one galaxy}$$
$$10^{11} \text{ galaxies} = \text{one universe}$$
$$(10^{11} \text{ is one hundred thousand million})$$

It is not surprising to find a large proportion of astronomy concerned with studies of extra-galactic nebulae or to find a growing number of radio astronomers with the same concern. The study of the distribution of the nebulae in space is the most fundamental of astronomical studies: it is the study of the structure of the universe.

Hubble photographed and classified a large number of extragalactic nebulae. They vary in shape from symmetrical, almost spherical assemblies of stars, through forms with a regular spiral structure, as in our own galaxy, to very open spirals and peculiar twisted and irregular shapes. The smooth nebulae are known as ellipticals, and are classified from E0 for a spherical shape, to E10 for highly flattened ellipses. The spirals are classified Sa, Sb, or Sc, in order of decreasing tightness of the spiral structure.

No nebula is completely described by this system alone, however, and the radio astronomer has often to deal with galaxies which do not fit into the sequence at all, and can only be described as 'peculiar'. The outstanding example is that of Cygnus A, which is not one nebula, but two, engaged in a violent collision. Cygnus A is such a powerful radio transmitter compared with our own Galaxy that we must separate it out from galaxies which are normal in the radio sense, that is to say galaxies which behave rather as our own does, and discuss it along with other prodigies in a later chapter. Of extragalactic nebulae similar in structure and behaviour to our galaxy, the Andromeda nebula, one of our nearest neighbours in extra-galactic space, deserves special mention.

The Andromeda Nebula

Our galaxy is a member of a small group of galaxies which seem to be associated locally in space, travelling together, and unaffected by the headlong recession of the more distant nebulae. The Andromeda Nebula (Plate 1) is the largest of our close neighbours in this community.

As about three quarters of all galaxies are spirals, it is not surprising to find that Andromeda is a spiral; it must, however, be counted a fortunate coincidence that it is a spiral of closely the same type and the same size as our own galaxy. It is seen at an inclined angle, so that the circular disc appears elliptical, but as seen from outside the spiral form is much clearer than we can hope to find it in our own galaxy. In the spiral arms of Andromeda, powerful telescopes can distinguish the bright O and B stars, many with ionized gas surrounding them. The fainter stars of the Population II extending through the whole nebula are mostly unresolvable, but show as a glow like our Milky Way, and enable us to delineate the shape of the nebula by photometric measurements of long-exposure photographs.

Presented with a galaxy like our own at a respectable distance instead of surrounding us, the radio astronomer has the possibility of elucidating some points of the large-scale structure of spiral galaxies, which at present are hidden from us. It is particularly interesting to find how far out the radio emission of the halo extends. The halo of our own Galaxy is seen from inside, and it is very difficult to find out how large it is without being able to step outside it and see it as a whole.

Radio emission from Andromeda was first clearly detected with the fixed paraboloid aerial at Jodrell Bank. The shape and size of the nebula were later explored with the new 250-ft steerable radio telescope, and also in Cambridge using the radio telescopes of the Mullard Observatory. It now seems clear that the radio nebula is considerably larger than the visible nebula, and that it appears roughly circular rather than elliptical. This accords well with the halo of emission in our own Galaxy, and shows that Andromeda has a magnetic field and a population of relativistic electrons extending far out beyond the visible nebula. This spherical region is so large that it covers the whole of the picture in Plate 1. The diameter of the visible nebula is about 100,000 light-years, while the halo is about twice this size. The total emission of radio waves is, however, somewhat less than in the Galaxy.

The spiral arms of Andromeda have also attracted the attention of radio astronomers concerned with the structure of our own galaxy. Leiden Observatory has an 80-ft paraboloid for its hydrogen-line receiver, and with this aerial the Andromeda nebula can be scanned with a beam about 4 minutes of arc across. The whole nebula is over two degrees across, so that it is possible to explore the motion of hydrogen in the spinning disc in the same

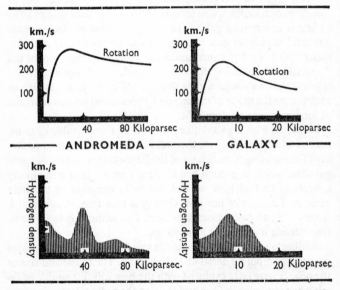

25. Rotation of the Galaxy and of the Andromeda Nebula. The rotational velocities and densities are similar, but according to present estimates the Andromeda Nebula is larger than the Galaxy

way as for our own spiral arms, and without the difficulties of interpretation arising from our situation inside a spiral arm. Figure 25 shows the rotation curve which has been found with this instrument; it also shows the density of hydrogen in Andromeda and in the Galaxy. The rotation curve may be used for deducing the distribution of mass through Andromeda, including of course, not only the visible mass, but the invisible gas and dust which make up an important part of all spiral nebulae.

The Magellanic Clouds

The Milky Way, seen from the Southern Hemisphere, appears to have two small patches detached from the main bright band of stars. These patches, known as the Magellanic Clouds, are in fact quite separate galaxies, and are our nearest neighbours in space. They are two of the smaller members of the community of galaxies associated with our Galaxy, of which the Andromeda nebula is the largest. They are irregular in shape, although some observers say that they show a faint spiral structure. At a distance of about 200,000 light-years, their constituent stars are easily resolved, and provide a valuable stage in the measurement of astronomical distances. Radio has been used in the exploration of these galaxies, both in 21-cm. hydrogen-line studies, and in broad band emission, and it has been found that the two Magellanic Clouds are linked together both by a tenuous gas and by a gravitational attraction which causes them to rotate about one another.

What is the essential difference between galaxies like the Magellanic Clouds, where the stars form into irregular masses, and galaxies like the Andromeda Nebula and our own, with their well-marked spiral structure? It may be just a question of age, or it may be a question of constitution. With the succession of types of galaxy, from irregular through Barred Spirals and Open Spirals to the tightly wound Sa Spirals, it is tempting to suggest that galaxies evolve along a sequence of types, just as an individual star evolves from 'young' to 'old' stellar types. Any examination of this idea raises the question of the composition of the various types of galaxies, and particularly whether they contain similar proportions of matter in the forms of hydrogen, dust, and stars.

For the Magellanic Clouds the 21-cm. line now gives us the chance of measuring the total mass of hydrogen gas in each nebula. This is quite simply done by measuring the total power received in the line radiation; it happens that the calculation of the mass from this one observation is a very simple one, and it is quite independent of the temperature of the hydrogen. The result is usually expressed in terms of the mass of the sun.

The Small Magellanic Cloud contains $1 \cdot 3 \times 10^9$ solar masses of hydrogen, and the Large Cloud contains $3 \cdot 0 \times 10^9$ solar masses of hydrogen. These figures are far more accurate than the estimate of the total mass of the clouds, which lies somewhere about 10^{10} solar masses for both. The figures for our own Galaxy show only about 2 per cent of the mass in the form of gas, out of a total of 10^{11} solar masses. At present it appears that there is a higher proportion of gas and dust in the irregular galaxies than in the well-developed spirals, the total mass in the Clouds being about one-tenth of the mass of the Galaxy. To draw any conclusions which might help the question of evolution of galaxies, we need these figures for more galaxies, including some of the same size as our own.

There are now several dozens of normal radio galaxies known, with measured values of radio brightness. The normality of their behaviour is quite remarkable, as the radio brightness bears the same relation to the optical brightness, within a factor of two, over a wide range of types of galaxy. When one considers that the light comes from stars, mostly near the disc or centre, and the radio comes largely from a gaseous halo, there seems no reason to expect such a close agreement. There are as yet no accurate 21-cm. line observations on these fainter nebulae.

Clusters of Galaxies

Amongst the known normal radio galaxies only a very few are elliptical, and these occur in clusters of galaxies. Clusters in fact usually contain many elliptical galaxies, and it rather looks as though galaxies are likely to develop into ellipticals rather than spirals when they find themselves in crowded conditions. It may be that these elliptical galaxies have collided with other galaxies, perhaps even several times in their lifetime, and that they have in these collisions lost the dust and gas which otherwise would have formed the spiral arms. The dust and gas would then be found scattered throughout the cluster, but not very much would be left in each galaxy. As radio sources, the elliptical nebulae would then be weak, but the cluster as a whole might be as strong as any other collection of normal radio nebulae. Here is an interesting line for experimenting, where a search would be made for radio waves from individual elliptical galaxies, and also from whole clusters.

The main difficulty in such an experiment is well illustrated by the story of the Perseus cluster. When a radio source was found in the exact direction of this cluster of galaxies, which is a prominent group at a distance of about 100 million light-years, and measuring only 2° across, it was natural to suppose that the whole group was radiating. There was some excitement about this discovery, as it appeared that the cluster radiated about four times as much as would be expected from a group of normal radio galaxies. However, Baade pointed out a peculiar galaxy in the centre of the cluster, and suggested that this galaxy alone was the radio source. Further studies, using an interferometer, showed that he was right – that 40 per cent of the radiation came from this nebula, NGC 1275, 15 per cent from another source of small angular size, and the remainder from an extended source; but the brightness distribution and flux density of this source do not agree with the expected radiation from the cluster of galaxies.

The story of the so-called Supergalaxy is another lesson in interpretation of radio signals from clusters of galaxies. This is a cluster whose very existence is a matter for argument, but it is supposed to be a cluster of some thousands of galaxies, and on a huge scale. It is in fact a cluster of clusters of galaxies. It covers many degrees of sky in the Northern Hemisphere, and if it is a radio source it should appear on several existing radio maps. Unfortunately the presence on these maps of a considerable band of emission at nearly the right place does nothing at all to substantiate the existence of the Supergalaxy. This particular band of radio emission is almost certainly connected with the Belt of galactic emission discussed in Chapter 6, and is nothing to do with any radio source or sources external to our Galaxy. Nevertheless the Supergalaxy was for several years considered to be a radio source, and much effort was wasted on theories of its radio emission.

The story of clusters should not be left on such a dismal note! In the Northern sky there is the Coma cluster, now definitely established as a radio source, and the story from the Southern sky is much more cheerful. The Sydney radio astronomers report that a well-known cluster of galaxies in Hydra and two clusters in Pegasus are all radio sources, apparently radiating about the expected amount for a collection of normal radio galaxies.

CHAPTER 11

Peculiar Galaxies and Colliding Galaxies

CATALOGUES of extragalactic nebulae usually give for each nebula a number, a position, a photographic magnitude, and a brief description of the type. The classification used is based on Hubble's series of elliptical and spiral types, and it is usually not too difficult to place a nebula in the series. It is, however, of no use to expect exact conformity between different specimens of one type; the closer the examination of any galaxy, the more individual it appears, and the more likely it is to have a little note beside its catalogue type, saying simply: 'Peculiar'.

Some peculiar galaxies are found which are not isolated from others, but linked in some way, either by a bridging arm of luminous matter or merely by gravitational attraction. This interaction occurs to some extent in the Magellanic Clouds, but it also occurs in spiral nebulae, which are much larger systems, and which can become quite fantastically distorted. Nothing more than a near miss between two galaxies is involved, but it is to be expected that galaxies will occasionally collide directly with one another. A close analogy to their random movement in space is the random movement of molecules in a gas such as air, but here direct collisions occur to each molecule about 10^{10} times per second. The frequency of galactic collisions is so low that many galaxies have never suffered a collision in their whole lifetime. The traffic is rather heavier than usual in clusters of galaxies, and here a galaxy has a more precarious existence. Here most galaxies will have suffered several direct collisions, and will probably have been changed entirely in appearance. We noted earlier that clusters contain a large proportion of elliptical galaxies: we must now look more closely at the explanation of this segregation of types on the theory of galactic collisions.

A collision between two galaxies sounds like a piece of science fiction, and one should perhaps refer to evidence of such occurrences before continuing an apparently speculative theory. The theory is largely due to Baade, and it was for some time unsupported by any direct observation of galaxies in collision. The first observation came as a result of radio astronomy.

The radio source in Cygnus was the first radio star to be found. It appears on the map made by Reber, in 1944, of extra-terrestrial radio waves of 500 Mc/s, but it was Hey who first recognized that it was a discrete source rather than a cloud of emission several degrees across. The accurate location of that source was a challenge taken up by radio astronomers in Sydney and in Cambridge. New aerials were built for radio star work in both laboratories, and the position of the Cygnus radio star was rapidly narrowed down to a small fraction of a degree. In that area, however, were many stars and extragalactic nebulae, and a casual glance at a photograph of the region revealed no object with any outstanding peculiarity to match a most remarkable radio emission. The only solution was to build a radio telescope which was specifically designed for measuring positions to the greatest possible accuracy, and this was undertaken by the Cambridge group. The experiment was rather like surveying, using a pair of exactly similar aerials at opposite ends of a 1,000-ft baseline (Plate 15A). The position of its baseline, and its length, had to be obtained as a basis of the survey of radio star positions. Results, which included the position of the radio star in Cassiopeia (see Chapter 9), were sent in 1951 to Baade, who decided that the accuracy at last justified the use of the 200-in. telescope. It is no use searching for a radio star with this instrument, whose plates cover a field of view only ten minutes of arc across, if it is necessary to make a dozen exposures each lasting many hours to cover the limits of error of the star position. It would take up too much valuable telescope time for a quite uncertain result. However, the new star position was believed to be accurate to within one minute of arc. On the first plate taken for this position, a nebula appeared at exactly the right place, and it was the most peculiar nebula ever observed.

Baade saw that this nebula, shown in Plate 4B, had two nuclei, and he realized that they were so close together that if they were two galaxies, they must be undergoing a direct collision. Full of enthusiasm for this first observation, he discussed this possibility with Minkowski, who challenged Baade for proof from the spectrum of the nebula. A famous bet was made, with the stakes a bottle of whisky. Baade won, for the spectrum proved to contain a series of emission lines which could only arise from gas in a very high state of excitation. A collision between two galaxies had been found, and a bottle of whisky changed hands.

Physical Conditions in Colliding Galaxies

A galaxy is largely composed of interstellar space, containing more or less gas according to the type of galaxy. The stars themselves occupy a very small proportion of the volume. Consequently, when galaxies collide, the stars pass one another quite unaffected, and apart from a very few near misses pursue their original courses throughout the encounter. During the high-speed collision, which may last for a million years, the interstellar gas and dust clouds will certainly interact. The real collision is a collision of these clouds and of the magnetic fields which they carry with them. There is sufficient kinetic energy here to explain all the radio waves from Cygnus A, which is the strongest known radio source, but the process by which the energy is converted is unknown. Quite probably the radiation is again from a synchrotron process, with both the magnetic field and the relativistic electrons being generated in the collision. There is no reason to suppose that this will occur in the visible part of the nebulae, and, in fact, interferometer measurements of Cygnus A show that the radio emission comes from two regions lying right outside the nuclei.

As far as the visible part of the nebula is concerned, our information about physical conditions comes from the spectrum. A large proportion of the light from the nebula comes from the gas between the stars, which is hot enough to emit spectral lines. These show that the temperature is greater than 10,000 ° K, which contrasts with the 100° K temperature of the hydrogen in our own Galactic plane. The exact wavelengths of the spectral lines should reveal the velocities of the two nebulae, but the gas is turbulent, giving blurred-out spectral lines. Probably they are rushing through one another at a rate of several hundred kilometres per second, some million miles per hour or so. One thing is certain –

there is no larger source of energy known to us than the release of kinetic energy in this tremendous collision. Only a small part is turned into radio waves, while most goes into heating the gas, and into violent turbulent motion of the gas clouds. This small part, for Cygnus A, amounts to 10^{37} watts, which would be the total power output from a whole galaxy of stars like the Sun, combining heat, light, radio, and every form of radiation. By the time this radio power has reached the earth, it has reached a less spectacular level: the power flux from Cygnus A over the whole surface of the earth is only 10 watts. Considering only the power incident on a large radio telescope, an acre in extent, the figure is reduced to 10^{-10} watts. And when a receiver selects only a small part of the frequency spectrum, for example, a bandwidth of 1 Mc/s at 80 Mc/s, the received power is as small as 10^{-13} watts.

The effect of the collision on the stars in the Cygnus galaxy is negligible, but it is amusing to speculate on the effect on living conditions on a planet like ours, if one such might be found in Cygnus A – a not unlikely circumstance. The high energy of the gas would, to some extent, be shielded from the planet by its atmosphere, which on earth absorbs many of the high energy particles and protects us from their harmful effects. But there would be such a bombardment by cosmic rays of all types that it is hard to imagine that life could be sustained. Anyone living under such conditions would find it an entertaining exercise to analyse the light from interstellar space and from the atmospheric aurorae, which would be greatly enhanced, and to find some detail of the acceleration of particles to such high energies, a process which is still a mystery to us. He would, however, find it hard to extend radio astronomy to any galaxy outside his own, for the noise level would prohibit any sensitive radio reception. Even radio and television broadcasting would be impossible under such conditions.

The Distance Record—3C 295

Recently Cygnus A has been deposed from its position as the most powerful and distant known radio transmitter. A very accurate position found for one of the radio stars in the Cambridge list, 3C 295, was used by Minkowski for another optical search with the 200-in. Palomar telescope. Exactly in the right spot he found another galaxy whose spectrum showed the unusual emission lines already found in Cygnus A. This time, however, the red shift of these lines showed a recession velocity of 0·45 of the velocity of light; the radio observation had tracked down the most distant galaxy ever observed.

This radio galaxy, faint as it is, can be seen to be the brightest member of a cluster of about sixty galaxies, so faint as to be scarcely visible on the 200-in. photograph. Only the brightest, with its powerful emission lines, yields a measurement of red shift, but the same value of red shift must apply to the whole cluster. Quite unexpectedly optical astronomy has available for cosmological investigations a group of galaxies at this great distance; radio astronomy may have done one of its greatest services to cosmology by directing attention to them.

The Red Shift

The interpretation of the red shift of spectral lines as a Doppler effect due to the recession of the galaxies has been a matter of controversy. As a crucial test of the Doppler explanation, an attempt was made by Lilley and McClain in Washington to find the radio spectral line from hydrogen in Cygnus A, not at the usual frequency of 1420 Mc/s but at 1390 Mc/s, as it should be after applying the optical red shift correction. Although they at first reported success, claiming that the hydrogen line had been observed in absorption at the correct frequency, more recent observations at Jodrell Bank have proved them wrong. The radio Doppler effect in a distant receding nebula still remains to be observed, and may indeed never be observed. We may soon find the theoreticians busy challenging the Doppler effect in light again, and we may find that the tempting promise of distance measurement by radio will come to nothing.

Regarding the measurement of distance, more will be said in Chapter 13, in connexion with the subject of cosmology and of the nature of the unidentified radio stars.

It hardly needs to be said that a considerable effort has now been put into the attempt to identify radio stars with visible objects, and particularly with extra-galactic nebulae. The Cygnus A and 3C 295 sources do not promise much success for any further identifications, as they are both such faint galaxies optically that fainter radio stars might be totally invisible. The results of the search have indeed been disappointing, but a few galaxies have turned up as radio sources, not quite as powerful as Cygnus A, but often with some rather interesting peculiarities.

Perseus A (NGC 1275)

There are several other definite cases of collisions among these identified extragalactic radio stars, but the only one which shows up well on a photograph is the radio star Perseus A, which is now known to be the galaxy NGC 1275. (The letters NGC stand for New General Catalogue, a catalogue of nebulae compiled by Dreyer and published in 1890.) This is shown in Plate 4A. This galaxy is much nearer than Cygnus A, at 170 million light years, compared with 550 million, and the plate shows quite considerable detail. The collision is between two spiral nebulae, one of which is a tightly wound spiral (type Sa) and the other a more open spiral (type Sc). The open spiral shows great distortion, as can be seen from the plate. The collision is energetic enough to excite the interstellar gas to radiate characteristic spectral lines, and from the apparent wavelength of these the velocities of the nebulae can be deduced. As they are so distant, both are receding from us, but the velocities of recession are quite different at 5200 and 8200 km./sec. The difference, which is the velocity of collision, is one per cent of the velocity of light. At this great speed, the collision will be all over within about one million years, a time which is short on the cosmic time scale. The same regions of this nebula appear to be responsible for the emission of light and of radio waves, unlike the Cygnus A nebula. This has been established both by accurate position finding and by actual measurements of the diameter of the radio source. Both by radio and by visible light the nebula appears about two minutes of arc across, so that its diameter is about 100,000 light-years, close in fact to the diameter of our own Galaxy.

Centaurus A (NGC 5128)

Nomenclature of radio stars varies between different observatories, but they all agree on the brightest radio stars in each constellation. These are called after the name of the constellation, with the letter A following. It will be evident from the headings of these sections that only the brightest radio stars are clearly identifiable with optical objects. Centaurus A is one of the brightest in the Southern Hemisphere, and its identification with the nebula NGC 5128 was one of the early successes of Bolton's radio star work.

The nebula well deserves the epithet 'Peculiar'. It appears as a nearly spherical nebula, like the type E_0, with a dark band stretching right across it. The best explanation for this dark lane is that it is another galaxy, a much flatter one, shaped like the spiral galaxies and seen from one edge, in front of, or mixed up with the spherical nebula. Evidence in favour of this is that the material in the dark band is rotating, rather like the rotation of our galactic plane, and that it has large random velocities on top of this rotation. If this interpretation is correct, we have another case of colliding galaxies; there must, however, be a sneaking suspicion that to find a collision exactly half-way through, with the dark line bisecting the spherical nebula, is an unlikely chance, and we may have to think again.

Virgo A (NGC 4486)

Here is a galaxy which is in a class by itself. It is an elliptical galaxy of type E_0, that is to say it is very nearly spherically symmetrical. There is no suspicion of a collision. The galaxy appears as an object about 5' of arc across (Plate 3B), and the radio source has about the same diameter. There is, however, a brighter blue streak or 'jet' to be seen protruding from the centre, and the light from this jet is polarized just as is the light from the Crab nebula. Only these two very different objects are known to radiate polarized light, and the inescapable conclusion is that NGC 4486 contains some powerful source of energy that can stimulate electrons to radiate synchrotron radiation, just as in the supernova remains. But there is no 'jet' feature on the radio source: the radio emission comes from the main part of the nebula, which must be filled with electrons with higher energy than those in our own Galaxy.

To summarize the situation regarding peculiar radio galaxies, we can say that a small fraction of extragalactic nebulae radiate more powerfully than our own galaxy, by a factor which ranges up to several million times for the most powerful yet known (Cygnus A and the recently identified 3C 295). Some of the least powerful radiate only a few times normal, and these are the galaxies which show the least optical evidence of high energies. The collision nebula in Perseus, NGC 1275, shows optical emission lines indicating a very energetic interstellar gas. Here the radiation is about one thousand times normal.

In Chapter 13 we shall be attempting to elucidate the nature of the very many radio stars which have not yet been identified with optical objects, and perhaps never will be. With such a wide choice of types of radio emission from galaxies, it might seem that this question is unanswerable; however, it will be shown that these unidentified radio stars most probably belong to the class of colliding galaxies, with an emission of the same order as that of Cygnus A. Before this argument can be presented, a summary of the experimental results of radio star surveys is necessary.

To conclude these two chapters on the identified radio stars, the following table gives the list of fairly certain identifications. It includes the results of recent work by the radio observatories at Cambridge, at Jodrell Bank, and at Sydney. The distances of the extragalactic sources have been computed according to the recently revised scale of distances resulting from work by Sandage. These distances depend on the value of Hubble's Constant, which relates velocity and red-shift to distance. Hubble's value was 540 kilometres per second per million parsecs of distance. Sandage now thinks that the correct value may be as low as 80, which increases all distances measured by red-shift by a factor of seven. This would increase the volume of the observable universe by several hundred times. As the new value for Hubble's Constant is still under discussion, the table was compiled using the round number of 100 for the Constant.

The Andromeda Nebula, M31. The nearest spiral nebula;
a galaxy like our own.

M81. A spiral nebula.

2

A NGC 3190. A group of four extragalactic nebulae in Leo.

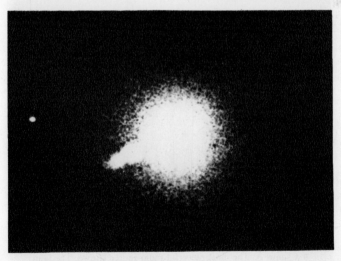

B M87. A peculiar galaxy emitting powerful radio waves. The bright 'jet' extending from the spherical nucleus emits polarized light.

A NGC 1275. Two spiral galaxies in collision.

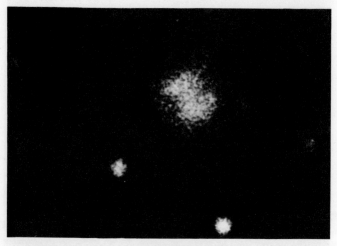

B Cygnus A. The most powerful radio source known. The faint visible nebula shows the nuclei of two colliding galaxies. Radio waves are emitted from outside the visible nebula.

Orion Nebula. A hot mass of ionized hydrogen gas in our own Galaxy. Visible in the Sword of Orion.

A Double elliptical galaxy. A newly discovered radio source. The two blobs of light to the right of the picture centre are complete elliptical galaxies connected together by a faint cloud of gas or stars.

B Trifid Nebula. A more distant hydrogen nebula (H II region).

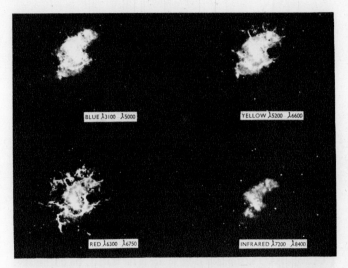

A Crab Nebula. The remains of a supernova explosion observed in
A.D. 1054. Four pictures using different colour filters show various parts
of the exploding mass of gas.

B IC 443. A radio source, believed to be the remains of a
supernova explosion perhaps 50,000 years old.

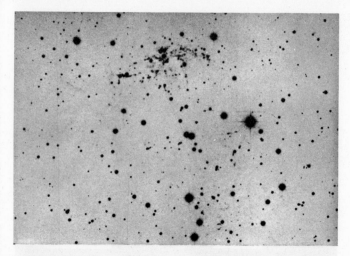

A Cassiopeia A. The strongest radio source in the Galaxy. On this negative reproduction the brightest part of the nebula shows as a mass of dark markings near the top of the picture. The nebula in fact covers most of the picture.

B The Solar Corona. The corona is seen at a time of total eclipse.

The Moon. Most of the surface seen here is a smooth desert of dust,
with a few small craters.

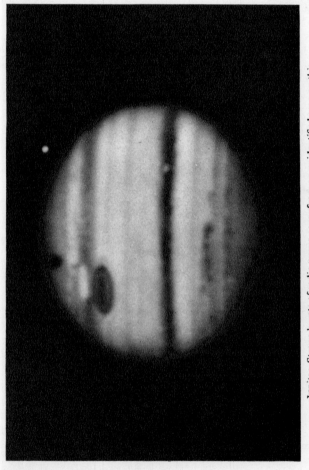

Jupiter. Strong bursts of radio waves come from an unidentified area on this planet. The famous Red Spot is seen in this picture.

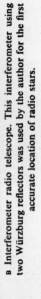

B Interferometer radio telescope. This interferometer using two Würzburg reflectors was used by the author for the first accurate location of radio stars.

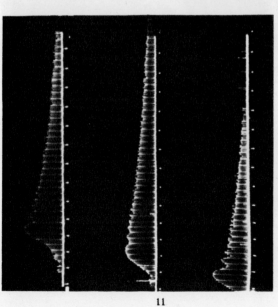

A Meteor Echoes. Radar echoes from a meteor trial, observed at Jodrell Bank. The signal grows smoothly and decays with characteristic oscillations of strength over a period of several seconds.

11

Owens Valley. The radio observatory of the California Institute of Technology. Two 85-foot reflectors mounted on railway lines, providing an interferometer with variable spacing.

Jodrell Bank. The spectacular 250-foot reflector radio telescope.

A Pulkova observatory. A section of a paraboloid surface. This reflector is used for observations of solar radio waves.

B Mullard Observatory, Cambridge. Radio star interferometer. Fixed aerial extending 1450 feet east-west.

A Mullard Observatory, Cambridge. Radio star interferometer. Mobile aerial, on 1000 feet of railway track running north-south.

B Mullard Observatory, Cambridge. Pencil beam interferometer using aperture synthesis. The mobile aerial is seen close to the centre of the 3300-foot east-west aerial.

15

Radiophysics Laboratory, Sydney. The Mills Cross pencil beam interferometer aerial.

SOME OPTICALLY IDENTIFIED RADIO SOURCES

1. *Unusual Extragalactic Nebulae*

Name	NGC Catalogue No.	Description	Distance (millions of light-years)	Diameter (thousands of light-years)	Radio emission (times normal)
3C 295	—	Colliding galaxies	4,500	—	500,000
Cygnus A	—	Colliding galaxies	550	150	250,000
Perseus A	1275	Colliding galaxies	170	60	800
Centaurus A	5128	? Collision between elliptical and spiral galaxies	10	75	25
Virgo A	4486	Spherical galaxy with blue 'jet'	40	120	200
Hercules A (uncertain identification)	—	Faint peculiar galaxy	800	50	100,000

Notes. 1. The distances and dimensions in this table depend on the value of Hubble's Constant, which is not accurately known. A value of 100 km. per second per kiloparsec has been used here.

2. The radio emission has been compared with the visible light emitted by each nebula, adjusting values so that our Galaxy would give a value of unity.

2. *Normal Extragalactic Nebulae*

Name	NGC Catalogue No.	Description	Distance (millions of light-years)	Diameter (thousand of light-years)
Our own Galaxy	—	Spiral (Type S_b)	—	75
Andromeda Nebula	224	The nearest spiral (Type S_b)	2	130
Large Magellanic Cloud	—	Irregular galaxies, the closest to our own Galaxy	$\frac{1}{8}$	40
Small Magellanic Cloud	—			20
M33		Spiral (Type S_c)	2	50
Companion to Andromeda	221	Small elliptical	2	8

Note. All these galaxies, of very varied types, give nearly the same ratio of radio to light emission. There are now about thirty of these normal galaxies, detected mostly by radio telescopes at Jodrell Bank and at Radiophysics Laboratory, Sydney.

3. *Radio Sources within the Galaxy*

Name	Catalogue Number	Description	Distance (light-years)	Age (A.D. 1960)
The centre of the Galaxy	—	Strong radio emitter (not understood)	30,000	—
Cassiopeia A	—	Supernova remains (Type 2)	10,000	About 260 years
Kepler A.D. 1604	—	Supernova remains (Type 1)	3,500	356 years
Tycho Brahe A.D. 1572	—	Supernova remains (Type 1)	1,000	388 years
The Crab A.D. 1054	M.1	Supernova remains (Type 1)	4,000	906 years
Gemini A	IC 443	? Supernova remains	6,000	? 100,000 years
Cygnus loops	NGC 6960 NGC 6992 NGC 6995	? Supernova remains	2,500	? 100,000 years
Orion Nebula	NGC 1976	H II region. Visible in Orion's Sword		—
Omega Nebula	NGC 6618	H II region		—
Rosette Nebula	NGC 2244	H II region		

Note. There are many other identifications with H II regions, such as the North American, Pelican, and Trifid nebulae.

CHAPTER 12

Radio Star Surveys

WE now enter the most exciting and the most difficult field in radio astronomy, that is the study of those radio stars which cannot be identified with visible objects. It is exciting and intriguing, for it offers the chance of a rapid solution to the fundamental problem of cosmology, and it is difficult because our knowledge of radio stars comes through radio telescopes, which must necessarily compare rather unfavourably in performance with the pin-hole camera. Furthermore, no two radio telescopes are built alike, and there certainly are no two radio telescopes that perform alike. To sort out the idiosyncrasies of one particular instrument with its own observers and extract from a published account of radio stars a true picture of the sky has not so far been possible. All that can be done is to look at all the best surveys and find the main points of agreement. Unfortunately, the whole crux of the cos-mological question lies at a point where there has been severe disagreement. An understanding of this difficulty, and a tentative solution to the cosmological problem, can only be approached through a detailed look at the experiments.

Interferometers

The first survey of radio stars was that of Bolton, in Sydney. He was building on previous work by Reber and by Hey, but his radio telescope was the first to be designed especially for radio stars. The word radio telescope in these days tends to suggest to us a large parabolic reflector, possibly because this type of instrument bears some resemblance to an optical reflecting telescope. But Bolton's radio telescope serves to remind us that no instrument designed specifically for detecting radio stars has in fact looked anything like this. His instrument was an interferometer. Details of this particular radio telescope may be found in Chapter 18, but essentially an interferometer consists of two or more separate aerials, at some distance from one another, which are joined to the same receiver. Another variation of this type of instrument was built soon afterwards in Cambridge, by Ryle, Smith, and Elsmore, who were able to use it to compile a catalogue of fifty radio stars.

The peculiar property of interferometers which prompts their use in place of single aerials for radio star work is that they can be made sensitive only to radio waves which come from sources of small angular diameter. The advantage of this is, of course, that the instrument rejects the intense radiation which forms a background to the radio sky and which largely originates in the galactic halo. The rejection of these large signals means that the signals from weak radio stars can be amplified and recorded without overloading the apparatus with much larger signals. But it is necessary to remember that the interferometer is specially designed to reject sources of large angular diameter, and 'large' may well mean greater than only a few minutes of arc. What if a radio star comes into the field of view with a diameter somewhere near this limit? The instrument will then record it at reduced intensity, and, in the absence of further evidence, the radio star will appear in the catalogue with its wrong intensity, or may even be missed out completely.

The Misleading Idiosyncrasies of Radio Telescopes

Having pointed out a specific difficulty in interferometers, which should really be taken as a warning to use their specific advantages with caution, it is necessary to balance the picture by pointing out some sources of error which occur in some degree with any radio telescope, whether it is an interferometer or a 'pencil beam' instrument. (The term 'pencil beam' means that the sky is scanned with a narrow receiving beam of the type which is obtained with a single parabolic aerial.)

Firstly, sidelobes. A sidelobe in the reception pattern of an aerial represents a direction in which an aerial is sensitive when it should be insensitive. For an example we may quote another early survey, that of Ryle and Smith when they first found the Cassiopeia A radio star. In the account of their results they also mention a radio star in Ursa Major, giving a position and intensity. Not long after publication they found that this radio star did not exist at all, but that the radiation from Cassiopeia A, received in a sidelobe response of the aerial, was simulating another radio star. It was some years before the Ursa Major radio star disappeared from lists of radio stars. There must be several of its kind in present-day lists, and it will be some time before they can be found out and expunged. Even where the sidelobes are known with some accuracy, they may prevent the detailed search for weak radio sources in parts of the sky adjacent to the more powerful sources. For example, the Andromeda nebula was a very difficult object to study with early interferometers, for the records on which it should have appeared were covered with the sidelobe responses to the radio star Cygnus A. It was not until the Manchester fixed 220-ft paraboloid was built, with greater resolution and lower sidelobes, that this nebula could be 'seen' at all in the presence of the 'dazzling' radio stars close by. All aerials have sidelobes. It is necessary in any radio star survey to know where these sidelobes are and how big they are. It may never be possible to remove all spurious radio stars from the catalogues, but it is vital to know how reliable the catalogue is and what proportion of its radio stars are genuine.

Secondly, confusion. This is a difficulty which is virtually unknown in optical astronomy, as it arises from the very limited resolving power of radio telescopes, combined with their peculiar way of recording the presence of a radio star by deflecting the pen of a recording ammeter. This recording is crude indeed compared with a photographic plate, which gives, at one exposure, a complete picture of a considerable area of sky. Usually in such a picture each star is clearly distinguished, or 'resolved', from its neighbours. The output of a radio telescope also derives from a considerable area of sky, but because of the poor resolving power of the aerial everything in that area combines to produce one single output. If there is one radio star in the area brighter than the others, that star will dominate the receiver output, but its record will nevertheless be confused by the combined effect of the others, and interpretation of the record can give errors both in brightness and in position of the star. Worse, the combined effect of the small radio stars may give the appearance of a single bright radio star, and a fictitious star may again then find its way into a catalogue.

The Cambridge Surveys

The precise effect of these distributing factors, sidelobes and confusion, cannot be known before any particular radio star survey is fully under way; the design of the aerial, however, takes detailed account of the results of the previous survey. Each increase in sensitivity and resolving power rests on a cumulative

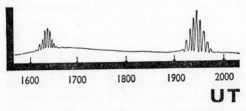

26. The radio stars Cygnus A and Cassiopeia A. This recording was made in the first Cambridge survey, using an interferometer at 3·7 metres wavelength

series of experiments. For the survey carried out in Cambridge in the years 1953–4, the design rested largely on results of the first Cambridge survey of 1950. Some records made in that first survey are shown in Figures 26 and 27. The responses of the two largest radio stars are seen, and, close to these responses, sidelobe responses can also be seen. The more serious problem of confusion shows up in the section of the record near the radio star Taurus A (the Crab Nebula), made with the same aerial, but with great sensitivity. Here there are obviously several radio stars on the record, but the small ones are all muddled up with one another, and the only way of sorting them out is to build a better radio telescope, with an angular resolving power adequate to separate out these confused radio stars.

The radio telescope which was built with this problem of con-

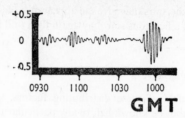

27. Radio stars in Taurus. An interferometer record from the first Cambridge survey. The large signal is from
the Crab nebula. A 'phase-switching'
receiver was used, giving an increased
gain over the previous records

fusion in mind was the large interferometer shown in Plate 14B.
This was used in 1953 for a survey at 81·5 Mc/s, known as the 2C
survey, and later for a survey at 160 Mc/s, known as the 3C survey. A large effort was put into the 2C survey, in which the sky
was covered several times over using different receiving and
recording techniques. Accurate positions were found for many
radio stars then seen for the first time, and detailed experiments
were undertaken to calibrate the sensitivity of the interferometer
and to find the effect of the ionosphere on the directional accuracy.
The result was a catalogue of nearly 2,000 radio stars, which
appeared in a special issue of the Memoirs of the Royal Astronomical Society. In the listing of these 2,000 radio stars, the
attempt was made to sort out very troublesome confusion, which
affected the records more than was anticipated; much of the
analysis was made from badly confused recordings like that of
Figure 28. About half of the 2,000 were suspected of being affected
in some way by confusion, so that either the positions or the
intensities quoted were expected to be somewhat in error, mostly
for the weaker stars.

The authors of the 2C catalogue were over-optimistic. It now
appears that only about 500 out of the 2,000 can be correctly listed
and that many of the others do not bear any close relation to
reality. Confusion was responsible for this. The mistake of analys-

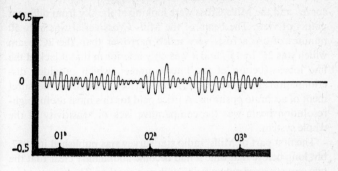

Sidereal time

28. Recording from the second Cambridge survey (2C). This interferometer record shows the effect of 'confusion' between adjacent star traces

ing too deeply was a natural one. It was, however, distressing to realize progressively how bad the catalogue was, as results were received of the next radio star survey, now to be described.

The Mills Cross Survey

In Australia there had been several small-scale radio star surveys in the early 1950s. The experience gained showed the vital importance of confusion and the need for a high resolving power. B. Y. Mills began an attack on this problem in an original way, with an aerial designed specifically to overcome this difficulty. The Mills Cross aerial, which was constructed for a survey both of the Galaxy and of radio stars, is an instrument of very great interest, for it was the first large radio telescope to make use of the technique of 'unfilled apertures', which will be explained in Chapter 18. The first Mills Cross aerial, shown in Plate 16, was designed for a frequency of 85 Mc/s, close to the 81·5 Mc/s of the 2C survey, but the telescope was of the 'pencil beam' type, with no special means of selecting small diameter sources from large ones. This, of course, was necessary for the exploration of the background radiation, but it meant that from the start the 2C survey and the Mills Cross were looking at the sky from different points of view. The beam of the Mills Cross aerial was only 50 minutes of arc across, very much narrower than the 2C beam which was $2\frac{1}{2}°$ by 15°, and it was only inferior in that it lacked the fine lobe structure of the interferometer, which provided discrimination against large diameters and also allowed the measurement of accurate positions. A price paid for this most useful high-resolution beam was the comparative lack of sensitivity of the whole system.

The first part of Mills' radio star survey was published in 1957, but long before that time it had become abundantly clear that the two surveys were not agreeing with one another. There was only a small patch of sky where the surveys overlapped, as they were made at latitudes no less than 86° apart, but in this patch only a very few of the more intense radio stars were seen by both surveys to be in the same place, and with the same intensity.

The history of radio star surveys now appears as a ding-dong competition between Cambridge and Sydney, with major surveys of increasing value coming from each in turn. This is a good example of the effect of a healthy rivalry in scientific research. Two laboratories working on the same general problem will inevitably develop their own ways of tackling them and will at the same time derive great benefit from following the results of each other's experiments.

In this case Cambridge's interferometer was overcome by the confusion trouble, while the next stage of the Mills Cross was almost clear of this at the cost of an increased noise level. The next Cambridge survey had to have an increased resolving power, and the design of the new Mullard interferometer began from this point. It was not necessary to wait for this new instrument before any advance could be made: the old interferometer could immediately be improved by converting it to work on shorter wavelengths.

The Cambridge 3C Survey

Changing the operating wavelength of a paraboloid reflector is easy; only one dipole is involved. To convert the Cambridge interferometer from 80 Mc/s to 160 Mc/s was a longer job, as 192 dipoles had to be made and installed; further, the parabolic reflector screen had to be improved for the shorter wavelength, and this involved stringing up no less than forty miles of wire. After about six months' work, the interferometer was ready for the next survey, called 3C, with a beam which was now half the former width in each direction. Again the sky was scanned several times over, and again the problem of confusion was the limiting factor in the analysis of the records. However, with a beam of one quarter the size it was possible in theory to find four times as many radio stars. With great restraint, a list of only 450 was made, with a fair degree of certainty that each one of the 450 was a real discrete source in the position given in the catalogue, and with the quoted intensity. At the time of writing, this list is the most reliable made so far, although it is estimated that about 15 per cent of the 3C radio stars may be appreciably in error. The growing caution of the radio astronomers is evident in a comparison of three largest lists of radio stars. The 2C, Mills, and 3C have contained respectively 2,000, 1,100, and 450 radio stars, even though they are listed here in chronological order. Further, it now appears that this list is in order of increasing reliability, although for the weaker radio stars the 2C survey is very far behind the other two in this respect.

But this remark prejudices the issue, and we must now look at the use which optical astronomers have made of these catalogues, and see what they have to say about the accuracy of the work of the radio astronomers.

The Search for Visible Radio Stars

An astronomer who tries to find visible stars or nebulae at the listed positions of radio stars is trying to find a needle in a haystack. Astronomers are, fortunately, most patient, and they will carry out such a painstaking search if they are fairly sure of finding at least one worthwhile needle amongst the heaps of uninteresting hay.

Look again at the problem of finding the galaxy Cygnus A, where the brightest extragalactic radio source was only identified when its position could be quoted to one minute of arc. Cygnus A appears as a very faint galaxy on the plates of the Palomar Sky Survey, a photographic atlas which covers the whole sky with pictures taken with the 48-in. Schmidt telescope. Now consider the problem when a radio star appears on two surveys at two different places, the accuracy of either being so poor that dozens of galaxies could be the visible part of the radio star. Contending with this situation Dr Minkowski of the Mt Wilson and Palomar Observatories was able to find only a very few identifications from the 2C and from the Mills catalogue, and he asked for radio positions agreed between Cambridge and Sydney before much more could be achieved.

In 1957, Dr Dewhirst from Cambridge Observatories went to spend a year with Dr Minkowski in Pasadena, provided with a revised Mills catalogue and the new 3C catalogue, and he was given access to the original plates of the Palomar Sky Survey. After a year of hard work, he found not one but several needles in the haystack, and, incidentally, did the greatest possible service to radio astronomy by providing an independent assessment of the reliability of the surveys. He was able to say that both lists agreed well for bright radio stars, and at least fairly well for many fainter ones. Taking the bright ones only, he used the accurate positions of 93 radio stars in the 3C catalogue, and after many weeks of detailed searching he produced a score card which read like this:

Identification previously made: (Cygnus A, Taurus A, etc.)	7
New identification with normal galaxies	6
New identification with unusual extragalactic nebulae	8
Radio stars in optically obscured regions	14
Radio stars with possible but improbable identifications	8
Radio stars with no optical objects brighter than 18th magnitude	50
	93

Total identified: 21   Total unidentifiable: 50

This represents the best score so far, and reflects a great improvement in recent radio data.

Several of the new identifications were with elliptical galaxies occurring in pairs or groups, representing a new kind of radio source (Plate 6A). The main puzzle left is posed by the fifty radio stars which are invisible, having nothing brighter than 18th magnitude in their position. The positions are reliable, as could be demonstrated from the identified radio stars: the result definitely showed that nothing at all was visible of these fifty radio stars.

The Future of Radio Star Surveys

Dewhirst's work can be said to mark the era when radio star surveys became respectable. However, the Mills Survey and the 3C survey by no means represent the end of this enterprise, and it is at least of historical interest to record here the present attempts being made to improve on them.

(i) In Sydney an interferometer using part of the Mills Cross is now in use for measuring the diameters of the radio stars in Mills' catalogue.

(ii) In the Mullard Observatory at Cambridge an entirely new interferometer has been at work since 1958. This powerful instrument is described in Chapter 18.

(iii) At Manchester the 250-ft paraboloid will be used for surveys on various frequencies. The measurement of diameters is to be extended by the use of new reflectors, used with the 250-ft paraboloid as high-resolution interferometers.

(iv) The University of Illinois, U.S.A., is constructing a single reflector with a collecting area of five acres, for work at about 70 cm. wavelength.

(v) The Lebedev Institute in Moscow is constructing a very large version of the Mills Cross, with a collecting area of several acres in the form of cylindrical paraboloid reflectors.

(vi) Pulkovo Observatory, near Leningrad, plans to make a reflector of about ten acres for radio star work.

The multiplicity of different radio telescopes all working on the same problem need not distress any one. We may expect disagreement and discrepancies, but they will be attributable to the fundamental differences between the operation of interferometers and pencil beams, and between single apertures and crosses. The pencil beams will map out everything which they have sensitivity enough to see; the interferometers will reject some large sources, but will give the best possible positions for the distant radio stars. All types will see deeper into the universe, and help to solve the riddle of the unidentified radio stars. Radio astronomers already believe that they are seeing further than any ordinary telescope can reach, and they hope that the next stage of observations, with increasingly powerful radio telescopes, may take them close to the edge of the universe. In this enterprise a keen rivalry between different observatories certainly exists, but there is growing realization that the spirit of international cooperation which pervades all astronomy is in the end the only guide to true understanding.

CHAPTER 13

Radio Cosmology – What are Radio Stars?

It may seem strange to head a chapter with such a question when four previous chapters have been concerned with detailed descriptions of various kinds of visible celestial objects, all positively identified with radio stars. The question is, however, one that has never been near a full answer on the basis of identifications alone. Consider the position in 1952. The five brightest radio stars in the sky had by then been identified with five different kinds of object: a pair of galaxies in collision, an elliptic galaxy with a blue jet, an elliptical galaxy with a dark obscuring lane across it, a supernova, and a strange galactic nebula. There were no other certain identifications, but there were clearly at least hundreds of detectable radio stars. The total number of radio stars certainly detected and located up to date (1959) is between one and two thousand, depending on the degree of certainty demanded, but out of this number, after the most intensive search, the total list of certain identifications only comprises eight galactic nebulosities, about forty extragalactic nebulae with normal radio emission, and fifteen abnormal extragalactic nebulae. By the time these words are published these figures will be out of date, but it is unlikely that more than a few per cent of the total number of radio stars will be identified during the next ten years, or indeed that they will ever be identified. With a wide range of classes of identified radio stars, it is reasonable to ask to what class belong the majority of the others. Are they in our Galaxy, perhaps close to us and belonging to a spiral arm, or more distant and representing a population spread wide through the halo of our Galaxy? Or are they very much more distant, perhaps as powerful as Cygnus A and at greater distances than even the 200-in. telescope can reach?

The evidence to be used in discussing this problem comes from the radio star surveys which were described in the previous chapter. Very little optical evidence is used, but it is worth pointing out some optical results which contain already a suggestion of the answer.

(i) The radio nebula Cygnus A is known to be at a distance of 550 million light years, whereas if it were at a distance only twenty times greater it would be at the edge of the observable universe.

(ii) Cygnus A is an 18th magnitude nebula, and if it were 21st magnitude, that is fifteen times fainter, it would hardly be seen at all by the Palomar telescope.

(iii) Many radio stars whose existence is established beyond doubt, and whose positions in the sky have been accurately determined, do not correspond with any optical object brighter than 18th magnitude.

The inference that many radio stars lie at distances greater than Cygnus A is not quite inescapable, but it certainly is reasonable, and it certainly is exciting. If it can be substantiated, it immediately puts radio astronomy in the position of solving a very difficult fundamental problem about the structure of the universe. To explain this implication a diversion into the subject of cosmology is necessary.

Cosmology

To the experimental physicist the universe thought of as a whole is a most unsatisfactory place. The most exciting challenge which any scientist can face is to attempt to describe the large-scale structure of the universe, to describe the physical laws which determine its observable features, and to infer the history of its evolution. The difficulty is that there is only one universe. Physical laws are formulated by comparing the behaviour of many different systems, and finding what is common to all of them. Experiments can then be made on further systems to show that this behaviour is predictable; for example gravity is observed to act on all massive bodies such as planets and apples, and we can therefore confidently predict the gravitational force acting on any other body. But there is only one universe, and we can find no laws of behaviour of universes in general. We can only describe what we can see, and relate it to our experience with more tractable physical entities.

To describe the universe we live in we must break the bounds of our solar system, and of our Galaxy, and look first for any information about the most distant regions. We cannot suppose the universe to have any boundary, for a boundary has two sides, and what would lie beyond? But there is a definite limit to the distance to which we can explore by any physical means; and this distance is set by the observed recession of the extragalactic nebulae. It was Hubble who first found that the more distant a nebula is from the Galaxy, the greater is its velocity of recession, so that an extrapolation of his observations suggested that at a certain quite definite distance the nebulae would be travelling away from us at the velocity of light. Their electromagnetic radiation, or indeed any other conceivable radiation, would then contain no energy for us to observe, and the nebulae would be to all appearances non-existent. This distance limit is now estimated to be about ten thousand million light-years. At lesser distances the light from the nebulae would be observable, but it would be reddened by the increase in wavelength to be expected from the Doppler shift. Our observational material for the study of the large-scale structure of the universe must be obtained from these receding nebulae.

A curious feature of any observation of a distant nebula is the historical information which it contains. If a nebula is, say, one thousand million light-years away, then our photograph of it is made with light that set off from it a thousand million years ago; our knowledge of the distant parts of the universe must therefore be dated progressively further back as the distance of our observations increases. This fundamental limit on our knowledge means that we can only attempt a description of the universe, making a simple picture or model, checking all the time that all the various observations fit the model. The different models proposed are known as 'cosmologies', and it is not surprising to hear from theoreticians that there is an infinite number of these possible cosmologies to be tested against observational data. It seems a ruthless simplification to bring the number down to two, representative of two kinds of model embodying quite opposite theories of the history of the universe, but simplification is necessary and has the advantage that we are left with two models easily understandable in concrete terms. The models are based on the 'steady-state' and 'evolutionary' theories of the origin of the universe.

It appears at first sight that the spectacle of the recession of the nebulae implies that a projection backwards in time of their motions shows that at a moment of time ten thousand million years ago they were all contained in a very small volume of space. Their departure from this region would then be the largest explosion conceivable, and represents the beginning of the history of the universe; as far as we are concerned this was the moment of origin of all the material of the universe. From this moment onwards, the nebulae receded from one another, and the universe 'evolved' towards its present state.

An alternative to this interpretation has recently been widely discussed. It is suggested in this 'steady-state' theory that the universe undergoes no such drastic change, and in its general appearance is the same at any time. To account for the loss of material which the receding galaxies take with them, the theory proposes the continuous creation of matter widely dispersed through the whole universe at a rate which is undetectable on a laboratory scale, but which on a much larger scale can provide complete new galaxies to replace the loss represented by the recession of older nebulae. The difference between these two models is fundamental, and gives such a contrast between the pictures of the distant parts of the universe that it allows observational tests to be made which would differentiate clearly between the two opposing theories.

We have seen that distant nebulae are observed as they were a long time ago, while close ones are seen as at comparatively recent ages. Suppose all nebulae came from one large explosion, and that since that moment they have receded from one another, evolving within themselves as they go. Then an exploration to fainter and more distant galaxies is an exploration backwards into this evolutionary process, and comparison of near and distant galaxies is a comparison in physical conditions in the present day with those of an earlier stage of the universe when, as we have seen, the nebulae were both younger and more tightly packed together.

On the other hand, if matter is being continuously created

everywhere in the universe, keeping the general appearance constant everywhere, the physical conditions everywhere can be supposed to be unchanging; the average age and separation of nebulae will not then depend on their distance from us. This 'steady-state' cosmology therefore implies a uniformity of behaviour in complete contrast to the variation with distance inherent in the explosive 'evolutionary' cosmology. The energies of optical and radio astronomers alike are directed at the problem of deciding which accords best with observations, and it is the suggestion that many radio stars may lie at greater distances than do the faintest visible nebulae that promises that the answer may already be within our grasp.

The Statistics of Radio Stars

Stellar statistics, the discipline of counting stars in order to find their distribution in our Galaxy, is a formidable subject. All statistical counts gain in precision by the use of large numbers; classical astronomy allows large counts of a large number of different classes of object, and much of our knowledge of stellar motions and of the distribution of stars in the galaxy attains its detail and precision from careful statistical argument. When we think of applying statistical arguments to radio stars, we must recognize from the start that the conclusions can only be simple generalizations, and that these will inevitably be challenged on the grounds of insufficient data. Nevertheless radio star statistics are of the greatest interest, for we are coming to believe that they are the statistics of the furthest portions of our universe.

The expanding universe is often compared with an infinitely large plum pudding, growing uniformly as it cooks. Each plum represents a galaxy, and each plum is surrounded by plums retreating steadily from it, uniformly in all directions. Each plum moreover will think itself the centre of the pudding, as not only are the motions of the other plums radially outwards from itself, but their velocities increase in proportion to their distances. It is only if the pudding has an observable edge that any plum could in fact have the right to claim a position at the centre. This model serves to remind us that distant nebulae are observed distributed

uniformly over the sky, and that the number seen out to a certain
distance increases simply according to the volume of space out
to that distance. Moreover the distance also determines the intensity I of radio waves from the nebula. But we have seen that in the
most distant parts of the universe we may find it worth while to

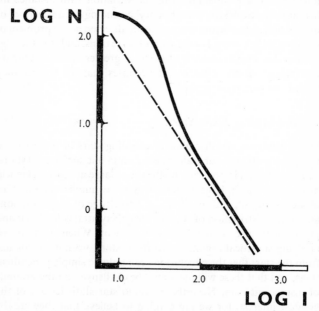

29. Radio star statistics. Plot of number N against intensity I,
showing an excess of weak radio stars

look for differences in the age, and therefore the state of expansion, of the plum pudding, and the number of nebulae will not
increase by such a simple law. The simple law states that the
number N is proportional to the minus three-halves power of I,
so that a logarithmic graph of N against I would have a slope of
minus 3/2. In an evolutionary universe the law would not be so
simple, and the graph would not follow the same straight line.

The first opportunity to plot this graph came with the results of

148

the 2C survey, whose 2,000 radio stars appeared to be enough for a significant test of the law. Ryle announced the result in the Halley lecture in Oxford in 1955, when he showed the graph of Figure 29. This graph was obtained from radio stars covering most of the sky visible from Cambridge, but it was also possible to show that the same graph was obtained from all separate parts of the sky except near the Milky Way, where galactic radio stars are found. The graph showed not a slope of $-3/2$ as expected, but a

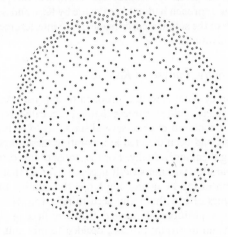

30. Distribution of the galaxies in an evolutionary universe

slope of about -3; the top part of the graph where the line tails over can be ignored, as this is the region where the radio stars are too weak to be detected individually. A slope of -3 indicates that the radio star population increases with increasing distance, that is to say that we are in a kind of spherical hole where there is a comparative dearth of radio stars. How big the hole is needs further argument, but Ryle showed good reasons for suggesting that it is at least 300 million light-years across, implying that the increasing number of radio stars seen at low intensities are all at distances comparable with limits of the observable universe. This would give a picture of the universe like Figure 30. If on such a scale the universe is found to be so non-uniform, the 'steady-state' hypothesis of the universe must immediately be abandoned, and the 'explosion' theory is given strong support.

Unfortunately it did not all turn out as simply as that. Here we meet the clash of opposing experimental results referred to in the previous chapter. The Mills survey in Australia did not confirm the shape of the curve, and moreover it showed that the 2C catalogue was more in error than anyone had suspected. Much of the value of the 2C survey would have vanished at this point, if an entirely new approach had not been made by Ryle and Scheuer to the analysis of the actual records made by the interferometer in the survey observations.

The Probability Analysis of Records

The 2C survey records were a problem to analyse because they showed so many radio star traces that at practically every part of the record a confused trace of several stars was to be found. The first analysis had been directed at separating these stars out and cataloguing them individually. For the statistics this detailed and careful separation was not strictly necessary, for all that was used in the graph of log N against log I was the number of stars at various values of I, without any need to refer to their catalogue numbers and positions. Ryle and Scheuer, finding that cataloguing was an uncertain process, decided to miss out the catalogue entirely and work straight from the records.

Statistical theory was now put to work to find how radio star records combined, and to produce a relation between the amplitude of composite or confused records (Figure 28) and the distribution of radio stars in space. The relation is expressed in Figure 31, which shows the expected probability P of obtaining various records, deflections D for the 'steady-state' universe, along with the curve obtained from the records themselves. Again a difference was found, which agreed rather surprisingly well with the previous analysis, based on the unreliable 2C catalogue. The universe still appeared to be non-uniform, and the evolutionary theory was still upheld; the situation is now fully confirmed by the 3C survey and by the results from the new interferometer at the Mullard Observatory.

It should not be thought that this is the only attempt that has been made on the cosmological problem. Optical observations of distant nebulae have been concentrated on essentially the same search for differences in the near and the distant regions of the universe, differences in population density, in luminosity, or in

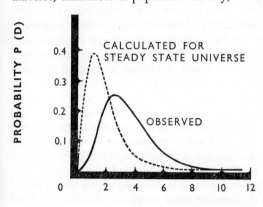

31. Analysis of 'confused' recordings of radio stars. The observed probability distribution of record amplitude is compared with the theoretical curve for a steady-state universe

the appearance of galaxies at the extremes of the observable range of distance. The strongest argument for the construction of the 200-in. telescope was that it could be used to extend this range well beyond that of previous instruments, which had clearly failed to demonstrate any cosmological effects of distances. Optical observational tests of the theories of the universe have had a hard time. There have been years of painstaking effort, in which the feeling about the final outcome has swung from one side to the other, for and against the steady-state cosmology, without any definite answer so far. The struggling radio astronomer may take heart from this, for he finds his fortunes fluctuate in just this way. The conclusions from the probability analysis were not final, for another objection was raised as soon as they were published.

The Diameters of Radio Stars

Between Australia and England there has been a healthy rivalry in radio astronomy right from the beginning of its development in 1946. The separate laboratories have kept in close touch, but quite naturally have gone their own ways in designing radio telescopes and in their choice of experiments to perform with them. Sometimes, but surprisingly seldom, this may be a wasteful procedure. For radio stars it has provided the most interesting situation of two entirely different techniques applied to the same problem, and finding answers which at first sight are so different that each side must be tempted to say that the other's experiments are at fault. Instead, the differences serve to show the weaknesses of each other's experiments, and in this question of the statistics of radio stars measured either by counting or by probability analysis the weaknesses centre on the sensitivities of the different instruments to the diameters of various kinds of radio star.

It will be recalled that Mills in Australia used a 'pencil beam' aerial, made in the form of a cross, whereas the Cambridge observations were made with an interferometer. The difference in behaviour is that the interferometer is designed to observe only radio sources which have a small angular diameter, and to reject larger ones, whereas the pencil beam accepts all sources. The question now arose that as the surveys differed quite markedly in any comparisons made on any selected area of sky common to both, there might be some selection of data; such a selection could come from the chance of the diameters of some radio stars lying in a range such that the interferometer would reject them and the pencil beam accept them. These differences are still not completely understood, but certainly something of the sort does happen, and separate experiments have been undertaken to measure the diameters of various types of radio star so that this complication can be resolved. In principle these experiments are performed by using an interferometer whose length of baseline may be varied by moving one aerial, but it is not easy to move an aerial whose area is many thousands of square feet. (It is not impossible – see Plate 15A.) A fair approximation to this experiment has now been found by relating the results of several different interferometer surveys at different frequencies and at different spacings; such a roundabout procedure may not be ideal, but the guesswork involved in such interpretations is now reinforced by detailed results from the new Cambridge radio telescope which is used both as a pencil-beam instrument and as an interferometer.

Firstly, it is clear that the differences between the interferometer and pencil-beam surveys are partly quite accidental results of sidelobes and confusion, which become progressively sorted out as radio telescopes become better understood and as better instruments are built. Secondly, there are real differences due to sources with large diameters, perhaps about 1° or more. However, these sources are almost all found in the Milky Way, and they cannot affect the cosmological question. Outside the Milky Way, where the counts are made, there are no sources with diameters which would confuse the interferometer observations. This means that the statistics from the interferometer surveys are the right ones to use for finding the statistics of the distant extragalactic radio sources.

If radio stars are indeed extragalactic and if the diameters are not troublesome, there is good reason for the suggestion that the statistics of radio stars already provide the answer to the cosmological problem, and that the answer so far is in favour of 'explosion' rather than 'steady-state'.

What are Radio Stars?

The argument about statistics must not be allowed to cloud over the real issue of this chapter. Perhaps the statistics will be proved wrong: it must not be thought that all our present clues to the nature of radio stars would then be removed. Starting from undisputed facts it is possible to prove that the unidentified radio stars are at very great distances, and that they must be correspondingly powerful, perhaps more powerful even than the Cygnus A radio star. The reasoning is based on these facts:

(i) Radio stars are to be seen in roughly equal numbers in all parts of the sky, excepting the Milky Way, where known Galactic sources of radio waves add to the total. This fact is referred to as the 'isotropy' of radio stars

(ii) The total radiation from all radio stars in space cannot be greater than the total background radiation. Part of this background comes from a halo surrounding our Galaxy, which from our eccentric position, nearer the edge than to the centre of the galaxy, does not appear isotropic. It is conceivable that the invisible radio stars we are trying to locate fill this halo, with only a very few extragalactic nebulae added to their number, and if we explore this possibility the halo radiation must be taken as the total radiation from all radio stars. Alternatively, if the radio stars are supposed to be extragalactic, only the isotropic component of the background radiation must be thought of as the total effect of radio stars

(iii) Lastly, although radio star statistics are not very reliable, they do give some idea, within perhaps a factor of two or three, of the intrinsic luminosity of an average radio star, provided only that the density of population of radio stars in space can be specified.

Meagre facts although these may seem, they provide surprisingly useful evidence. We can use this to say not so much what radio stars are, but what they are not. Figure 32 shows a graph which enables any answer to our question to be represented by a dot, the horizontal axis representing the average intrinsic luminosity of a radio star, and the vertical axis their average density in space. For example, if radio stars are very common occupants of the universe, their point will be found near the top of the diagram. If they are the rare and distant objects we have been supposing, and if they are very powerful sources of radio waves like the Cygnus A source, their characteristic point will be in the lower right-hand part of the diagram. The scales of the diagram are rather unusually compressed, representing the wide range of possibilities open to our present state of ignorance of the radio universe. The scales are plotted logarithmically, so that the range of intrinsic luminosities varies by a factor of 10^{15} which is approximately the ratio between the energy generated in a collision between two galaxies, and in the thermonuclear furnace of the sun. The range of densities corresponds to average distances between radio stars from one to 10^8 parsecs (400 million light-years) corresponding to the distance of the nearest stars and of the faintest nebulae visible in the 200-in. telescope. The regions of this diagram which may be occupied are limited by our three facts stated above and also by the reasonable supposition that the radio stars must conform to the visible universe by being found in one

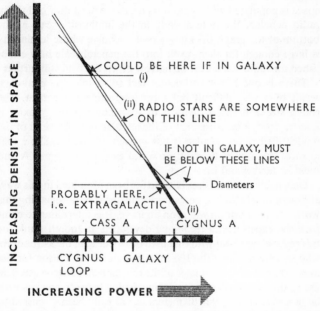

32. The nature of the radio stars. The majority of radio stars must be very rare objects with very high emission, possibly higher than the colliding galaxy Cygnus A

of three places, spiral arms, haloes of galaxies, or distributed throughout the universe.

The thick line corresponds to the measured intensity of radio stars (observation iii), and the other two observations (i and ii) limit the position along this line in the ways shown. Conclusions from this graph still need more observations to sharpen their precision, but so far the graph shows that radio stars are not spiral arm objects and that they do not belong to the Galactic halo.

In the graph their characteristic point must lie well down in the right-hand corner; the argument now assembles any auxiliary evidence to find any limits on the density with which extragalactic space is populated with radio stars or, as we must now call them, radio nebulae. We note already in the luminosity scale at the bottom of the graph the known radio nebulae whose luminosity is large enough for them to fit into the general scale now established for radio stars. Can we narrow down the field still further?

There is one last experimental fact to fit into the picture, a result of a very difficult but most interesting experiment. The rough size and shape of most of the known radio galaxies is known; from a measurement of the angular size of several of the unidentified radio nebulae it has proved possible to show that most of them must be more powerful even than Cygnus A and must lie far beyond it.

Only a few radio sources have so far been examined in this way, although in Australia a new interferometer is now beginning this work and the position will soon improve. It is interesting to compare the experimental technique developed at Jodrell Bank for this radio experiment with that used by Michelson, the astronomer who in 1923 adapted the 100-in. telescope of Mt Wilson for the measurement of the diameter of the red giant star Betelgeuse. The use of the interferometer for distinguishing between sources with large and small angular diameters has already been discussed in this chapter: it is easily seen that the extension of this technique to an actual measurement of diameter is only a matter of increasing the spacing of the aerials in the interferometer until the interference pattern is so fine that the source counts as large in comparison with the width of the interference fringes. Michelson measured the diameter of Betelgeuse to be 1/20 second of arc: for radio galaxies we can expect that very few will be found with diameters less than about 5 seconds of arc, which means that the radio interferometer need only extend over one hundreth the distance, measured in wavelenths, used by Michelson. This sounds as though the experiment is easy, but a look at Figure 33

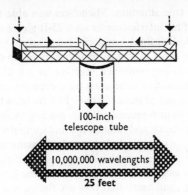

100-inch
telescope tube

10,000,000 wavelengths

25 feet

MICHELSON'S INTERFEROMETER

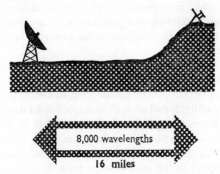

JODRELL BANK   CAT AND FIDDLE INN

8,000 wavelengths

16 miles

THE RADIO INTERFEROMETER

33. A comparison of the sizes of Michelson's stellar interferometer and
the radio interferometer used by the Jodrell Bank Observatory

157

will show the true situation. Michelson was able to mount the two mirrors of his interferometer on a 25-ft girder on the 100-in. telescope: at Jodrell Bank one aerial is kept fixed at the observatory, while the other is moved to out stations up to forty miles away, the two being connected together by a radio link. So far ninety-one unidentified radio stars have been examined with this instrument, and out of these thirty-eight have been found to have diameters less than 6 seconds of arc, placing them well beyond Cygnus A in distance and luminosity, and quite possibly for ever outside the range of optical observation. If many radio stars are found to be so small in angular diameter, then their place on the diagram will be established firmly in the extreme lower right-hand corner, and we shall know that they are the most distant observable objects in the universe.

Radio Red Shift

It may be wondered how it comes about that radio astronomy with quite limited observational results should so soon have grown into a position where it is presuming to answer deep cosmological questions, while in comparison optical observations carried out in such detail by telescopes of great sensitivity and resolving power should have failed to penetrate so far towards the edges of the observable universe.

The key to this problem lies in the 'red shift' of the spectrum of distant objects, which is the result of their velocity away from us. Near the edge of the observable universe, this velocity approaches the velocity of light, and all radiation has shifted its spectral content right down to very low frequencies, that is, to very long wavelengths where radiation contains only very little energy. At intermediate distances, the strongest part of the optical spectrum has been shifted to the infra-red spectrum, leaving a greatly reduced intensity in the visible region. For radio wavelengths the the spectrum is of quite different form, which varies with frequency much more slowly than in the short wavelength region of the optical spectrum.

The Present Situation

In conclusion, it is premature to say that radio astronomy has given an unequivocal answer which clearly chooses between theories of the universe. Radio astronomy, however, has been shown to be the most likely approach to cosmological problems, because of its undoubted ability to penetrate further than any optical instruments, and indeed it may be that the present results which tend towards the 'evolutionary' rather than the 'steady-state' theories are within sight of full confirmation.

The difficulties of these radio investigations may perhaps have been under-emphasized in this brief account. The need for bigger and better radio telescopes will be fairly evident from the chapter describing the radio star surveys which provide the raw material for the present cosmological speculations. Improvements are certainly possible, but in what direction should they be made? Should we aim to count as many faint radio stars as possible, or should some particular wavelength be chosen, or a measurement of diameter be attempted?

If we consider the problem of the receding galaxies, and fix our attention on one particular galaxy, we may ask how its appearance will change with time, and how this change will differ as between the different cosmological theories. At the point when the galaxy is approaching the speed of light, and is becoming increasingly more difficult to observe, the differences will be large; this region is probably for ever inaccessible to observation. Closer in, we have seen that the population density in which the galaxy is found may be a useful indicator, and that the surveys may already have found significant changes in population with distance. Here the new radio telescopes are required simply to increase the numbers counted. There are, however, two other indicators which might prove useful; these are the spectrum and the angular diameter of distant radio stars.

There is a possibility that the radio spectrum of an extragalactic nebula may vary with its distance, on account of the red shift changing the spectrum in a recognizable way. Such a change could then be used as a measure of distance, providing a radical improvement in the whole cosmological analysis. Here the radio telescope would be required to make penetrating surveys on a wide range of frequencies under comparable conditions, instead of making one survey on a single convenient frequency, chosen so that sensitivity and resolving power are balanced against one another. Finally, the measurement of angular diameter may be used as a distance indicator, as indeed it has been used in this chapter. If diameters of extremely faint radio stars can be measured, and these radio stars are nebulae moving with more than one half the velocity of light, the diameters may be expected to produce some very direct evidence for cosmology, as they should show the peculiarity of an *increasing* apparent angular diameter with increasing distance. There will therefore be a minimum angular diameter which any radio star can have, and the value of the minimum will depend on the cosmology of the universe. Designing a radio telescope which will achieve the necessary accuracy for this measurement on very weak radio stars seems to be out of the question at present.

CHAPTER 14

The Moon

OUR nearest neighbour in space, the moon, is now emerging from a long period of neglect by astronomers. It used to be regarded as by far the best clock available to us, moving round the earth in an orbit which, if complicated, was nevertheless predictable, so that the time at which it cut off the light from the fixed stars could be used for setting our most accurate clocks. The atomic clocks have changed our attitude, and we now tend to find the irregularities of the earth's rotation along with the finer points of the moon's motion by using ammonia or caesium oscillators to mark out the even passage of time.

The motion of the moon is its best-known and best understood characteristic. Admittedly there are extremely detailed maps of the moon's surface, made by the most painstaking efforts of very many astronomers, including amateurs. New maps of the surface both of the front and the back of the moon are now being made. But the precise nature of that surface eludes us, the precise form of the mountains and craters is unknown, and worst perhaps of all we do not even know what the moon is made of. And the moon is an important body to us, far more important than the distant stars and nebulae, about which, in some respects, much more is known. We could perhaps manage without moonlight, although this would seriously inconvenience poets, farmers, and lovers, but losing the tides with which the moon enriches our shores would be too much for a seafaring and holiday-making nation.

The geometrical part of the description of the moon which has been arrived at from conventional astronomy is quite precise. The moon is travelling in a nearly circular orbit round the earth, at an average distance of 240,000 miles. This is not an impossible distance for a good motor car to cover in its life time, and it is also within reach of modern rockets, which can reach the moon in two or three days. From this distance, and from the angular size of the moon's disc, which is about $\frac{1}{2}°$, it is easy to show that the diameter of the moon is 2,160 miles, about a quarter that of the earth. The surface has two distinct types of topography, the 'seas' and the mountains (Plate 9). The 'seas' are large areas which appear nearly featureless, as would an ocean or a sandy desert seen from a great distance; they have fairly definite boundaries where they meet the mountainous regions. A few scattered volcano-like hills known as craters are found in the 'seas', but the rough mountainous regions are literally pitted with them. The craters are vast in size, but in form they are rather like large meteor craters on earth, such as the Arizona crater. Some are fifty miles across, and their depth from floor to the rim of the encircling mountain ring may be up to four miles.

Sunlight on the moon's surface undergoes a cycle of $29\frac{1}{2}$ days' duration, and this cycle which is like the daily cycle on earth is manifest to us by the changing phases of the moon. Only one side of the moon is present to us, as the gravitational forces which keep it in orbit also pull one face more strongly than the other and prevent rotation.

Turning to the radio observations of the moon we find results which at first simply accord with the findings of conventional astronomy, but eventually the use of wavelengths about one million times that of light waves has given a new picture of the surface of the moon. Let us take a look first at the radio investigations of the atmosphere surrounding the moon, and then at the measurements of its surface temperature. The radar observations, which promise to give the most detailed descriptions of the surface, are described last.

The Moon's Atmosphere

We are all familiar with one of the minor difficulties that will beset the first travellers to reach the moon – the lack of air. It is not at all hard to show this lack – one only need look at the edge of the moon through a low-powered telescope and observe the stars as they pass behind and are occulted by the moon's disc. If there were an atmosphere like our own, the stars would become fuzzy and their apparent positions would change as a result of the passage of their light rays close to the surface. No such effect is observed, and the most careful measurements at the moment of occultation show that there is no atmosphere greater than 1,000 millionth (10^{-9}) of the earth's atmosphere. Perhaps one should be content with this limit, because it already corresponds to as good a vacuum pressure as we can obtain in a physics laboratory with common techniques. But there are particular theoretical reasons for wanting to reduce the limit still further.

The gravity on the surface of the moon exerts a force only one twenty-seventh that of gravity on the earth's surface, and any atmosphere on the moon must be maintained there by this force alone. Working against this force is the thermal velocity of the gas molecules; for example in air at the temperature of the moon's surface the average velocity is about one-fifth mile per second, while if the molecules attain a velocity of $1\frac{1}{2}$ miles per second they can escape altogether from the moon. There is a wide spread of velocities about the average, so that a considerable proportion of air molecules would be leaking away, and any atmosphere would soon be lost entirely. (A similar leakage must occur from the solar corona, as discussed in Chapter 4.) Heavier molecules, such as those of the gases xenon and krypton, move more slowly, and would more easily form a lunar atmosphere. Curiosity drives us to look for an atmosphere of these rare gases, although something quite different might turn up if the limits of detection could be improved by a factor of a hundred or so. This improvement is made in the observation of the occultation of a radio star as it is covered by the moon.

This radio experiment is very much the same as the optical observation of a star just at the point of occultation, but the sensitivity to a lunar atmosphere is tremendously enhanced by the ionized state in which any lunar atmosphere would be found. This ionized atmosphere would have a potent influence on the rays from a radio star passing near to the disc of the moon, and would show its presence by cutting off the radio waves earlier than the expected moment of occultation. On 24 January 1956 the moon passed across the line joining Cambridge to the Crab Nebula, which is a strong radio source, and the radio waves were observed to be occulted for 59·6 minutes. According to calculation, the disc of the moon took only 59·2 minutes to pass over the nebula, and the difference of 0·4 minutes, although not large enough to be a certain and accurately measured difference, looked very much like the effect of a lunar atmosphere.

Interpretation of this result by Elsmore at Cambridge shows that the vacuum on the moon is in fact better than had been expected. If the time difference were real, this indicated an atmosphere 5,000 times less than the previous limit, that is to say two parts in 10 million million of the earth's atmosphere. This is indeed a small amount of gas: if the whole of the lunar atmosphere were collected together and compressed to our normal atmospheric pressure there would be just about enough to fill St Paul's Cathedral. Regrettably, we do not yet know what gas it is, but it would be unlikely to be found to be a breathable atmosphere even if it could be collected together.

One consequence of this radio observation is that we now know that the edge of the moon is nearly as precisely defined for radio waves as it is for light, so that occultation of radio stars can be used as a precise means of finding their positions and for exploring the distribution of radio brightness across them.

The Temperature of the Moon

There are many ways of measuring the temperature of a body which is accessible to laboratory experiments, but for an inaccessible body like the moon it is only possible to measure its electromagnetic radiation, for example in the infra-red region of the spectrum, and deduce from this its temperature by using well established laws of thermal radiation. At first sight this appears impossible for the moon, for it is obvious that the light which comes from the full moon is reflected sunlight and has nothing to do with the moon's temperature, while even the faint light from the disc of the new moon comes from sunlight reflected off the earth. Visible light, however, is in a part of the spectrum where the sun radiates very strongly, and the moon very weakly. The position changes rapidly as longer parts of the spectrum are considered, and infra-red observations already give the possibility of thermometry at a distance. Radio waves are almost entirely free from trouble from solar radiation; the appearance of the moon for our new radio eyes changes not according to the illumination at any part of the lunar cycle, but according to the surface temperature only.

The first radio measurements of the moon's temperature were made in 1948 by Piddington and Minnett of the Radiophysics

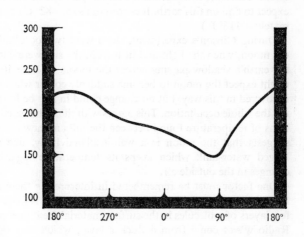

34. The radio temperature of the moon through one lunar month

Laboratory in Sydney. They used a wavelength of $1\frac{1}{2}$ cm. Subsequent measurements made in Russia and in America have used wavelengths of only 8 mm. A radio telescope for such short wavelengths is a very compact instrument, with a parabolic reflector only a few feet across and with a waveguide measuring about $\frac{1}{4} \times \frac{1}{8}$ in. inside picking up the radio waves at the focus. The beamwidth of the best instrument, used by Gibson in Washington, was only one-fifth degree, which is considerably less than the angular diameter of the moon, so that it was possible to explore the surface from one side to the other and to look for differences in temperature. The main experiment, however, was to watch the centre of the moon's disc throughout a lunar month, which gave a result like the other experiments following the graph of Figure 34. The graph shows variations in the moon's surface temperature with its changing phases, of about 30° above and below the level of 189° K, which is roughly the average surface temperature. (These temperatures are measured on the 'Absolute' scale. A temperature of 189° Absolute is about the lowest temperature one would ever expect to find on this earth. It corresponds to −82° C or approximately −116° F.)

During Gibson's experiment, there were two occultations of the moon, when the light and heat from the sun were cut off by the earth's shadow passing across the moon. Cold as it is, one might expect the moon to become suddenly colder when the sun is covered in this way, but no change could in fact be found during the whole occultation. This agrees with the rather small variations of temperature found between the full and new moon, and suggests that the moon is a well-insulated body, like a well-lagged water-tank which keeps its temperature regardless of changes in the outside air.

One factor must be remembered in interpreting these results. Light from the moon comes from the surface, that is from the top few layers of molecules in the surface material, be it dust or rock. Radio waves come from a thicker layer, which may be more than a whole wavelength thick depending on the material. The intensity of the radio waves is therefore determined by the average temperature of a surface layer at least several centimetres thick; for the shortest wavelength used so far, 8 mm., this thickness is about 6 cm. or just over two inches. When the sun's radiation is cut off the actual surface temperature must fall considerably, so that the constancy of the radio temperature tells us that the surface layer is a very good thermal insulator, preventing rapid changes of temperature from penetrating as far down even as one inch. Solid rock would not behave in this way. On domestic water tanks and between the rafters of roofs various kinds of granular substances are used to provide efficient heat blankets in our houses: if the air could be removed from the interstitial air spaces they would be very much more efficient. The most likely solution to the problem of the moon's surface is that it is covered with a layer of dust, which is at least several inches thick and acts as a most efficient insulation. It is an amusing thought that we can in principle explore the temperature of this layer at various depths down to several feet by measuring with progressively longer radio wavelengths.

The moon traveller is now provided with a further attractive feature in his travel brochure. He will step out of his rocket on to a sea of dust, and will probably sink into it at least up to his knees. Before he starts on this journey we should be able to tell him the temperature to be encountered by his toes as well as by his knees. They may be as much as 20° K different, but perhaps he will not mind the difference when both are so cold anyway.

Radar Astronomy of the Moon

A peculiar aspect of astronomy which gives it a unique place amongst the physical sciences is that it is impossible to do experiments on the subject of our investigations. We speak of astronomical experiments, and indeed no physical science can exist without recourse to some sort of experiments, but in fact these experiments are all observations of radiations from objects which cannot be reached in any way and whose motions and behaviour are quite out of our control. The astronomer has compensation for this difficulty in the multitude of different objects to be seen, so that if he wants to know what a certain star would do if its chemical composition were slightly different he can look around the sky and find another which gives the answer to his question without the need for experiment in the true sense of the word.

The moon used to be thought of as quite inaccessible. 'To reach for the moon' is now a phrase that has lost a little of its original poignancy, as we now contemplate sending rockets to do the first true astronomical experiments, such as collecting samples of the moon's surface, observing its behaviour when heavy objects fall on it, and of course a whole series of essentially geographical investigations if it ever becomes possible to land a man on the moon.

A rocket takes about $2\frac{1}{2}$ days to reach the moon, but electromagnetic waves take only $2\frac{1}{2}$ seconds to perform the double journey to the moon and back. The time for light or radio waves to travel to the nearest star is over four years, putting out of the question any possibility of sending anything to a star and back, be it rocket, light wave, or radio wave. The moon is the only heavenly body, apart from the man-made earth satellites, which is at present within easy reach of radar, although it is thought possible that several planets may eventually be reached.

The achievement of first detecting radar pulses reflected from the moon stands to the credit of a Hungarian, Z. Bay. It need not be emphasized that by the time a radar pulse has reached the moon, part of it scattered and part absorbed, and some of the scattered part has returned to earth, the power in the pulse that enters the receiving aerial is very small indeed and hard to detect against the random signals to be found in any receiver. Bay's solution to this problem was original and noteworthy. He decided to look only for pulses returning exactly $2\frac{1}{2}$ seconds after transmission, and, to sort these out from the receiver 'noise', he averaged the signals given by the whole instrument at several separate time intervals after transmission, and looked for an excess of signal at the $2\frac{1}{2}$-second mark. A long time was necessary for this averaging to be completed, and the signals were therefore added up for over half an hour in water voltameter cells. The detection of moon echoes was demonstrated by the relative amounts of gas liberated in the different cells. Chemistry does not appeal to most electronics experts, so it is not surprising to hear that the method has not been copied in other moon radar equipments.

An American Army radar made contact with the moon at very nearly the same time as Bay. The method was more conventional, and the difficulties of detection were overcome by the use of a larger aerial and greater transmitter power. These two experiments were the forerunners of a series conducted in the three observatories of Sydney, Jodrell Bank, and Washington, which have been primarily responsible for the more precise investigations of moon radar echoes, from which come some remarkable new ideas on the form of the moon's surface.

The outstanding characteristic of the echoes received from the moon is their variability. They fade in the same way as long-distance shortwave transmissions, and their amplitude can fall to zero instantaneously and rise several times above the average immediately afterwards. This behaviour was first investigated by Rayleigh as a part of probability theory, and it is often called Rayleigh fading. It is characteristic of simultaneous transmission over several paths together, combining in varying relationships to give additive or destructive interference according to the different lengths of the paths. In a notable Australian experiment, in which the broadcasting station 'Radio Australia' was used as the transmitter, groups of three pulses were sent up to the moon; the returned signal was fading so fast that quite often out of a group of three only two would be heard, one having apparently got lost on its long journey. The speed of fading is proportional to the radio frequency being used and also varies according to the peculiar motion of the moon known as libration.

Libration is an oscillation of the moon, a rocking of the moon's face from side to side so that the visible part of the moon includes positions at either side which periodically come into view. A full cycle of libration brings into view about 58 per cent of the moon's surface. During the cycle there are times when the surface is moving at about $2\frac{1}{2}$ m.p.h. across our line of sight to the centre of the moon, and others when it is momentarily stationary. The speed of fading is greatest when the libration velocity is greatest, confirming the suggestion that the fading is caused by the relative motion of different parts of the surface responsible for the multipath transmission. At Jodrell Bank it was shown that the speed of fading could be used to find how much of the moon's surface was effective in returning an echo; from this work J. Evans made the first suggestion that the moon was not behaving as might have been expected. It seemed to be rather shiny, more like a mirror than a rough textured sphere with a rugged surface covered with mountains and rocks. A more direct approach was possible when the Naval Research Laboratory published results of radar work using very short pulses. A radar pulse takes longer to return from the limb of the moon than it does from the centre, by 11½ milli-seconds. The first experiments had used pulses which lasted much longer than this, and it was impossible to sort out the part of the echo which came from different parts of the moon's surface. The new experiments used pulses only 10 microseconds long, giving a resolution of more than one thousandth part of the depth of the moon. Individual echoes still showed fading, but an average echo showed that the only parts of the moon which contributed significantly to the echo were those lying within 10 miles of range,

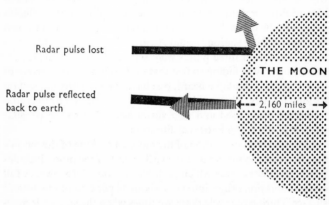

Radar pulse lost

THE MOON

Radar pulse reflected
back to earth

←-- 2,160 miles -→

35. The reflection of a radar pulse by the moon

corresponding to about 10 microseconds travelling time. Figure 35 shows how little of the moon's surface can be reflecting the radar pulses back in the direction of the earth. An area of about 200 miles across contributes over half of the total echo.

Being wise after the event, it is easy to point out that this be-haviour is exactly what would be expected from a moon whose surface is covered with sand or dust, which is after all the most likely surface. The surface will be smooth but greatly undulating, and all but the sharpest mountain peaks will have their sides smoothed over by gentle slopes of powder. The absence of any appreciable atmosphere on the moon means that 'weather' is an unknown quantity there. No winds or rains disturb the quiet deserts of dust. To a visitor from Earth the landscape must surely be forbiddingly bleak, silent, and cheerless. For radio waves a smooth dusty surface is as good as a mirror provided that there are no rocks or other irregularities more than a fraction of a wavelength across; the radar reflections show that roughness on this scale is quite rare. The apparent smoothness also suggests that over large areas of the moon's surface there are no slopes steeper than about 5°. Admittedly, terrestrial slopes are not often much greater than 5° if averaged over several miles, but inside shorter distances any sort of gradient can be found. To make the earth look like the moon it must be desiccated, sandpapered, and sterilized.

The Moon as a Relay Station

If it should become possible to land relay broadcasting stations on the moon, so that a radio programme beamed on to the moon would be re-broadcast with even quite a small power, such as could easily be derived from solar batteries, a shortwave programme could be received with clarity over half of the earth simultaneously. This may well happen in a few years' time, but for the moment it is instructive to speculate on the use which could already be made of the moon as a passive reflector of radio waves. Shortwave radio communications are never as good as they should be; interference, fading, and occasionally complete fade-outs make it very hard to converse easily at any time between countries not fortunate enough to be linked by a coaxial telephone cable. Communications over long distances are still so chancy and variable that any possibility of extending the range of transmission of waves too short to be reflected by the ionosphere would be welcomed. In 1954 the Naval Research Laboratory showed that speech could be relayed via the moon, by picking up the reflected signals from an ordinary transmitter working on a frequency of 220 Mc/s.

It is recorded that Alexander Bell, on making the first telephone link between two towns, opened the circuit with the words 'What hath God wrought'! No record exists of the words used on the first speech circuit via the moon, but it must be admitted that this was the lesser revolution in communication history. Before the discovery of the shininess of the moon's surface it was supposed that the lengthening of all reflections from the moon by 11·6 milliseconds would so distort any speech that only very slow transmission of information would be possible. Now that the lengthening is known to be only 100 microseconds it is apparent that a communication circuit is available which is capable of transmitting normal speech and possibly even music with very little distortion. Modulation frequencies of up to 10 kilocycles, higher than those passed in a normal radio receiver, could be transmitted without attenuation. There are, however, considerable difficulties.

The first difficulty in a moon relay circuit is to obtain enough power for communication to be established at all. This certainly means highly directive aerials, high power transmitters, and sensitive receivers, all of which are possible to make, even if they may be difficult or expensive. Secondly, the signal will fade so deeply that it will be necessary to provide at least two circuits working simultaneously to ensure that a signal can be received at any time. (This is the technique of 'diversity' well known in long-distance radio links.) But whatever we achieve technically, the final limitation is the fact that there is only one moon, and this one moon will almost certainly not be visible from both terminals of the communication link, just at the time when the link is most needed. This is a problem which is rather outside astronomy and is in reality a challenge to the users of radio communications to adjust their demands to fit in with a timetable depending on moonlight rather than sunlight. The possibility of moon echo links is certainly there, and in the present difficult state of radio communications there can be little doubt that a use will be found. Yet again basic scientific research will pay a practical dividend of a quite unexpected kind.

The Distance of the Moon

The last part of the story of moon radar takes one's thoughts back to classical astronomy. The distance of the moon is not a yardstick by which the size of the universe is measured, as is the distance from the earth to the sun, but it is a distance which can be related directly to the size and shape of the earth. Classically the distance was found by a triangulation method (Figure 36), in which the baseline was a large measured distance on earth. The determination of this distance requires the size and shape of the earth to be known; the angle between directions of the moon seen

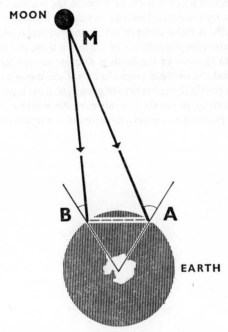

36. The distance of the moon found by tri-angulation. The separate distances AM and BM can now be found by radar

from either end of the baseline then gave the distance quite simply.

The distance to the moon now can be measured by the time taken for a radar pulse to reach the nearest part of the surface and return to the transmitter. This involves accurate time-keeping and also a powerful and sharp radar pulse, so that its arrival back can be precisely timed. The velocity of radio waves in vacuo is known, but some slight slowing-down of a radar pulse might occur in the ionosphere. These difficulties can all be met, and an accuracy of two parts in a million has already been achieved, corresponding to an accuracy of half a mile in distance.

Remembering now that the radius of the earth is 4,000 miles, it is clear that to find the distance between the centres of the earth and moon by radar involves a knowledge of the shape or 'figure' of the earth. A radar observation at one particular place can be used to determine the distance of the moon if the distance of that place from the axis of the earth is known; conversely it can be used to find the distance from the axis if the moon's distance is known. A possibility exists here of geophysical exploration via the moon, whereby radar stations all over the world can combine results to produce a new determination of the figure of the earth.

CHAPTER 15

The Planets

THE planets and their movements have been familiar to men for so many hundreds of years that it may seem surprising that so little is known about their composition and, in particular, about their surface conditions. Astrologers have always assumed a position of authority in planetary matters, and in recent years the fertile minds of science fiction writers have been filling in many of the gaps in our knowledge with fascinating detail. The scarcity of hard facts gives them enormous scope.

Astrophysicists like to point out that we know less about the interior of the earth than we know about the interior of the sun, or indeed of any other star. They rightly emphasize not so much the limitations of geophysics but rather the astonishing success of recent theoretical calculations of the generation and radiation of heat out from the central furnace of a star; the comparison with our terrestrial ignorance is startling nevertheless. When we come to consider the planets the situation is much worse. It cannot be claimed that radio astronomy greatly improves this situation, but it does play a more important part than might have been expected a few years ago. Much of the pre-radio knowledge of the planets comes from the study known as Dynamical Astronomy, or Celestial Mechanics, whereby from the motions of the planets in their orbits round the sun their masses can be found, and combining mass with diameter the density can also be found. From the density and appearance, some idea is then obtained of their composition. This is complemented by spectroscopic study of the composition of their atmospheres. The detection of radio waves from some of the planets adds a small, perhaps speculative, amount to the knowledge we have of the planets, but holds promise of further discoveries as sensitivity in receiving equipment is improved.

If we compare the inert sphere of the earth with the dramatic explosions of stars and the collisions of galaxies in outer space, we could hardly expect any radiation from the earth to be significant in comparison with theirs. The planets are, however, quite warm enough to generate thermal radio waves which can be used to measure their surface temperatures, and indeed one planet produces radiations that are rather more spectacular than the dull background of mere thermal radiation. Even if the future of radio astronomy should include exploratory rockets relaying back more detail about conditions on the planets, our reliance on straightforward observations of emitted radiation must be counted as absolute at present, with increased sensitivity the main hope for increasing knowledge. Let us see how far these observations can take us.

The results of dynamical and optical astronomy are briefly outlined first, so that the contribution of radio astronomy will take its place among these.

Dynamical Astronomy

It may seem strange that much of our knowledge of the interior of the planets, though not of their surfaces, comes from dynamical astronomy. Both the mass of a planet and its volume can be deduced from observations of the planet's orbit round the sun and of any moons or satellites around the planet itself, and from these a measure of its average density is made. For some, the very low density implies that most of the observed spherical object must be an extended atmosphere surrounding a much smaller rocky core, and interesting differences in the constitutions of the planets have been shown up in this way. Venus, for example, has been found to have a density approximately $5 \cdot 2$ times greater than that of water, which is very close to the $5 \cdot 5$ observed for our own Earth, while Jupiter, Saturn, and Uranus and Neptune all have densities between $0 \cdot 7$ and $1 \cdot 4$ times that of water. In their case, any solid rocky material which they possess must be in a small dense core, surrounded by ice, water vapour, ammonia, carbon dioxide, and other light-weight materials.

Surface Temperature

The measurement of the temperature of the surfaces of the planets is of great interest to astronomers. It has been achieved by an optical method which can also be used at radio wavelengths. This method has already been referred to concerning the measurement of the moon's temperature by using its radio emissions; for optical measurements the long optical wavelengths, that is the infra-red radiation, or heat waves, are used.

If a planet remains at a fixed distance from the sun, and if its surface is all at the same temperature, there will be a balance between the heat received from solar radiation and the heat lost by radiation to outer space. This balance will determine the tem-

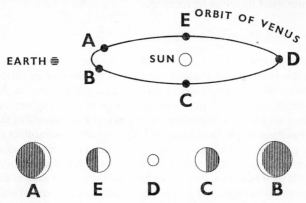

37. The phases of Venus. When Venus is nearest to the earth, as at C or D, only a crescent is lit by the sun. The dark part would be very cold if the planet did not rotate

perature, and this equilibrium temperature will fall off as the square root of the distance from the sun. A different temperature would be reached if the planet were not rotating but continually faced one side to the sun, just as the moon presents only one face to the earth. In this case, which may be true for Mercury, and might also be expected for Venus, one side will be very much hotter than the other.

Venus travels in an orbit of radius 67 million miles, while the radius of the earth's orbit is 93 million miles. As Venus is so much nearer to the sun than we are, it is always to be seen in the general direction of the sun, which means that it must be observed just after sunset or just before sunrise. According to its position in its orbit, it exhibits phases like those of the moon (Figure 37). When it is nearest to us its dark side only is seen, and when it is furthest it presents its sunlit side to us. In between, Venus appears as a crescent shape of illuminated surface. It is quite possible to detect the heat radiated by the dark side and compare it with that of the sunlit side. It is not possible to achieve very great accuracy in this measurement, but results do make it clear that the dark side is much warmer than it would be if it were permanently in darkness. Venus must therefore be rotating.

The Atmospheres of the Planets

Spectroscopy adds considerable detail to the optical evidence on the physical and chemical conditions on the surface of the planets. When sunlight strikes the surface and is reflected to the observer on earth, it passes twice through any atmosphere the planet may have. The presence of any gaseous constituent of the atmosphere would then be made known by the spectral lines of the gas, which appear as lines of absorption in the reflected solar spectrum. They will, of course, not be the only lines of absorption, as the solar spectrum already contains the Fraunhofer lines of the coronal absorption, and it must also contain the absorption lines of our own atmosphere. Nevertheless, a comparison may be made between direct and reflected sunlight and the extra absorption then reveals the planetary atmosphere. On the whole these atmospheres are unattractive to us, as the main constituents have been found to include, besides oxygen, carbon dioxide, nitrogen, and water, the unpleasant gases of ammonia and methane.

Thermal Radio Waves from the Planets

The planets all emit radio waves. Earth is unique in its profusion of man-made radio transmissions, to be found throughout the whole wave-band available to radio astronomy, and Jupiter is unique in the intense sporadic bursts of 20 Mc/s radio waves, which will be mentioned later. But all planets, whether or not they have their own peculiar emissions, must radiate thermal radio waves, and the intensity of this thermal radiation can be used to measure the temperature of the planets, just as the infra-red heat waves have previously been used.

At radio wavelengths, thermal radiation from hot planets is governed by the law which is known as the Rayleigh–Jeans approximation. This says that the flux density of radiation varies as the inverse square of the wavelength, and implies that for a given aerial size the received intensity increases as the square of the frequency. When we bear in mind the feebleness of the thermal radiation from the Earth itself, so slight that it is hardly ever noticed by radio engineers, and when we consider the great distance of the planets, it is surprising that their thermal radio waves can be detected at all. However, the Rayleigh–Jeans law leads us towards the shorter wavelengths, and detection of the planets has been proved possible at the short wavelength of 3 cm., using some of the most sensitive radio receiving apparatus yet constructed.

The first achievement of measuring thermal radio waves from planets was in May 1956, at the Naval Research Laboratory in Washington. Mayer, McCullough, and Sloanaker, using the 50-ft parabolic radio telescope, detected first the radiation from Venus, and, in a series of experiments lasting through to March 1957, measured the surface temperatures of Venus, Mars, and Jupiter. Apart from the difficulties of discriminating between wanted signals and interfering ones, including solar interference, these observers were hard put to it in the discrimination of the planetary radiation from the random fluctuations in their receiver.

Planet	Radio wave-length	Aerial tempera-ture (°K)	Planetary temperature (degrees absolute)	
			Radio	Infra-red
Venus	9 cm.	0·28	580 ± 230	240
	3 cm.	3·5	560 ± 73	
Jupiter	3 cm.	0·51	145 ± 26	130
Mars	3 cm.	0·24	218 ± 76	260

These fluctuations were at a level corresponding to changes of aerial temperature of only one-tenth of a degree Centigrade. The Table gives the main results of these first observations.

The aerial temperatures quoted in degrees above absolute zero show the accuracy and delicacy of observation achieved in this work. The uncertainties in the planetary temperatures are certainly rather high, but they are no worse than the accuracies of the previous determinations from infra-red observations.

Rough as they are, these radio measurements tell us several interesting things. Firstly, the general agreement between infrared and radio temperatures for Jupiter and for Mars gives some confidence in the experimental techniques and in the correctness of radiation theory applied to planetary surfaces. Secondly, the observations of Venus were, naturally enough, made when Venus was nearest to the Earth, and consequently showing her dark side to us. This dark side was certainly hot, confirming the impression that Venus is rotating. Observations were continued until Venus showed a crescent of sunlit surface, occupying 36 per cent of the apparent disc, and no large change of temperature was found in this time. Apparently the planet rotates fast enough for the temperature to remain fairly even, rather as on the surface of the moon.

Thirdly, and most strikingly, the radio temperature of Venus is more than double the infra-red temperature. Here again we are brought up sharply against the difference between the radio and the optical universe. Just what are we looking at with our new radio eyes? In the view of Venus which our conventional telescopes affords us, we see unbroken cloud covering the whole planet. The disappointing uniformity of this sheet of cloud makes it impossible to detect the rotation of Venus from direct visual observation, as no markings of any sort are visible. But clouds are no obstacle to radio astronomy on Earth and cannot obstruct our radio view of Venus. The radio telescope gives us, in fact, the first observation of the hitherto invisible solid surface.

One of the strangest facts about the surface of Venus is that this is apparently much hotter than the clouds above it. How the surface can reach the temperature at which lead melts, when the clouds above it are ice-cold, is hard to explain. Perhaps if it were understood there would be some new suggestions for making efficient greenhouses, with cool glass and hot interiors; possibly a new principle in solar furnaces will be found, whereby water can be boiled by the heat of the sun and some of the solar energy be utilized in electric generators.

Further Observations of Thermal Radio Waves

These first successes were shortly followed by some most promising new work with two new kinds of radio receiver. Sensitivities of $0 \cdot 1°$ K have for some time been accepted as a workable level for metre wavelength receivers and as a barely possible level for centimetre wavelengths. The two new receivers were those using, respectively, a Travelling Wave Tube, and a Maser. (See Chapter 19.) They both reached sensitivities approaching one hundredth of a degree, which is ten times better than the previous levels. With such a sensitivity an 80-ft radio telescope could easily detect the thermal radio emission from an iceberg 1,000 miles away.

One of the most remarkable features of the development of the Travelling Wave Tube receiver was that it was carried out by a private firm in America, the Ewen Knight Corporation, and that the receiver was developed solely for its use in radio astronomy. As a result, the firm found itself in a position to supply the newly-formed National Radio Observatory in America with one of the most sensitive receivers ever built. This new receiver has already been used on a paraboloid 28 ft in diameter, and it will be used on the new 140-ft paraboloid when this is completed in 1960.

The Maser receiver was developed at Columbia University, and it was first used at the Naval Research Laboratory in Washington. Here it was installed in the same 50-ft reflector used in the first detection of radiation from Venus. It will be seen from the description of the Maser in Chapter 19 that this installation is no mean feat. The important part of the receiver was mounted at the focus of the paraboloid, high above the ground, where it had to be kept immersed in liquid helium to keep it at an even temperature, only $1\frac{1}{2}$ degrees above absolute zero.

Both of the new receivers have been used to confirm the measured surface temperature of Jupiter, but, at the time of writing, the high temperature of Venus is only partly confirmed. The Maser receiver has been used for this at 3-cm. wavelength, and does indeed give a temperature of 575° K. However, some other observations at 0·86-cm. wavelength give the lower temperature of 410° K, not much higher than the boiling point of water (373° K). The different results obtained at different wavelengths require some explanation before either temperature is accepted as the true surface temperature of Venus. One quite simple explanation may well be the true one: that the shorter wavelengths are absorbed by the clouds which cover the surface of the planet, so that at 0·86 cm. a smaller proportion of the energy radiated by the surface actually gets away. If this is so, then it becomes possible to learn more about the cloud layer itself by its absorption of radio waves of various wavelengths.

The Travelling Wave Tube receiver has added one more planet, Saturn, to the list of radio successes. The mere identification of Saturn as a radio 'object' does not add much to our knowledge of the planet, but it does represent a great achievement in sensitive detection of radio waves. The rise in aerial temperature when directed towards Saturn was only one twenty-fifth of a degree.

This new receiver has already given an indication of the way in which new fields are opened up by such remarkable improvements in sensitivity. When the new Greenbank 140-ft reflector is in use, the detection of planetary radiations will be an everyday occurrence, and will in fact be extremely useful in calibrating the sensitivity of the receiving apparatus and in checking the directional accuracy of the aerial. Other small visible objects may also become usable for these purposes, and a grid of reference points will then be set up over the sky.

The new receiver using a 28-ft reflector has already detected radio waves from two galactic nebulae of a type known as planetary nebulae. The planetary nebulae have nothing to do with the planets or our solar system and are in fact rather like small H II regions. Those measured so far have the names of Helix and Dumb-bell, from their optical appearance.

All these observations at centimetre wavelengths are very much in line with classical astronomy. The brightest objects in the radio sky, the sun and the planets, are those which are also brightest visually, and the radio observations give their temperatures in the same way as infra-red measurements. Positional work is conducted in very similar ways, involving great accuracy in pointing an instrument, telescope or radio telescope, to any desired direction. This is in considerable contrast to metre wavelengths, where radio telescopes must of necessity depart from the traditional form of a fully steerable reflecting surface. Most of the radio observations of Jupiter have been made at wavelengths at this other extreme of the radio spectrum and give a picture totally unlike the optical appearance of any heavenly body.

Radio Flashes from Jupiter

But for a fortunate accident, nothing might have been known of Jupiter's radio flashes. They are still quite unexplained, and were certainly not a feature of the radio sky to be expected and to be sought out deliberately. The accidental discovery, the work of Burke and Franklin of the Carnegie Institution in Washington, was the result of a nice piece of detective work.

These two observers were experimenting with a new type of receiving aerial of a type similar to the Mills Cross which had just been built in Australia. This aerial was designed for the rather low frequency of 20 Mc/s as an exploration of radio astronomy technique at the long wavelength end of the radio spectrum. As I was responsible for the design, I may describe the aerial as being of quite crude construction, but it was specifically designed to have a beam width narrower than 2°, and was to be used firstly for the measurement of the intensities of radiation from several known radio stars. The aerial was difficult to align, and it was decided to leave it at a certain definite directional setting for some time, receiving signals from the same piece of sky day after day. It was midsummer, and the obvious choice for this strip of sky was that containing the sun. In midsummer the sun reaches a north declination of 23°, and just near this declination there are also two bright radio nebulae, the Crab nebula and the nebula IC 443. So the aerial was set at 23° and left, and, as it happened, it was left set that way for two months.

All sorts of signals, wanted and unwanted, were picked up by the aerial during this time. But one mysterious signal, apparently an untraced source of interference, erratic, and resembling car ignition or electric drill interference, appeared for a few minutes each day. It came at a time when no known source of interference was anywhere near the aerial, and from the timing of its appearance it could not come from any fixed position in the sky. Burke and Franklin, in their detective work, noticed that Jupiter's declination at that time was quite near to 23°, and when they compared its movements with those of the unknown source of interference they found an exact agreement. To their astonishment they had the first recorded radio signals from Jupiter, without having intended to look at planets at all, and they had in fact the raw materials of a whole new branch of radio astronomy.

The announcement of this strange radiation set radio astronomers all over the world directing their aerials towards Jupiter, but with surprisingly little success. It turned out that the coincidence of the aerial setting with the direction of Jupiter was matched by another coincidence – the frequency of 20 Mc/s was in the centre of a quite narrow band of frequencies on which the planet was found to radiate. With an aerial of greater beam width the radiation would never have been distinguished from genuine interference; the combination of beam width, declination setting, and frequency was essential but entirely fortuitous.

It so happened that in Australia, several years previously, the frequency of 18 Mc/s had been used for recordings of cosmic rays and these records were now carefully scanned for any signs of Jupiter signals. Originally insignificant and quite unrecognized, these signals were clearly to be seen. Moreover, as the 18-Mc/s recordings were made over a whole year, they were searched for variations in the signals, and some of the characteristics now well established were obtained from these early records.

Thunderstorms on Jupiter?

During a thunderstorm sharp crackles may be heard in radio receivers. The Jupiter signals seemed at first to be very like these. The records in Figure 38 shows sharp spikes from pulses of about one second in duration. This can be observed for one hour or more at a time, followed by several quiet hours, just as would be expected from a thunderstorm. The energy in the storm would have to be of truly Jovian proportions for a lightning discharge to be recorded so far away; a rough calculation gives a factor of 10^{14}

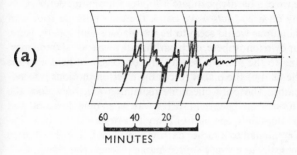

(a)

60   40   20   0

MINUTES

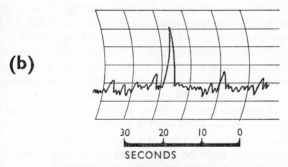

(b)

30   20   10   0

SECONDS

38. Radio waves from Jupiter. (a) Recording of circularly polarized signals, using an interferometer. (b) Recording of an individual pulse

between the power in a Jovian flash and a terrestrial flash. This suggestion of a massive discharge must be dropped, however, as it was soon found that the signals are in fact quite unlike lightning signals.

Firstly, the spectrum is unlike any known radio spectrum. On either side of 20 Mc/s the power falls off to an undetectable level at about 10 Mc/s and 30 Mc/s, almost as though there were a deliberate choice of frequency, as in a broadcasting station. Secondly, the radiation is circularly polarized, just like sunspot radiation.

Since we can hardly postulate a Jupiter transmitter deliberately radiating on a 20-Mc/s wave band, the only possible source of these radiations would seem to be the planet's ionosphere. Here, as in our own ionosphere, each part has its own special frequency, according to the number density of electrons, and here also the magnetic field of the planet forces the electron motions into circular paths. The only questions remaining are, how does the Jovian ionosphere behave in such a way when ours does not, and also why does only one part of it do it? For as well as the radiation being limited to a rather narrow wave band, it is also limited geographically to a single source at one place on the planet.

Jupiter rotates about once every ten hours; day and night come rather more rapidly there than here. The rotation is easily observed, as there are conspicuous markings, such as the famous Red Spot, which have been observed for many years (Plate 10). Strangely enough, the period of rotation found from watching these markings differs according to their latitude, and it seems that the visible surface acts as a liquid. Observations show that the surface near the equator rotates in 9 hours 50 minutes 30 seconds, while that at the poles takes 9 hours 55 minutes 40 seconds. The radio waves are only observed when one side of the planet faces us, and the periodicity as measured by the radio waves is 9 hours 55 minutes 30 seconds. This period places the source of the disturbance well away from the equator, and fixes its longitude to a few degrees. It must lie somewhere in a band of markings containing the great Red Spot. It would have been gratifying to find that this position coincided with the great Red Spot, but in fact it only fits with more minor markings, which may indeed have nothing at all to do with the radio waves.

Jupiter has four large satellites, or moons, which can easily be seen with the aid of a small telescope or a pair of binoculars. These satellites, as they circle round the planet, appear to cross the visible disc, and there is a fair chance that when this happens a satellite might come between us and the radio spot. Such an occultation may well have been seen on one occasion, and if it does indeed happen it gives a powerful method of measuring the exact position and diameter of the radio spot.

Do other planets have similar radio emissions? As far as we know the answer is no. Sharp radio impulses from Venus have been recorded by one observer only, and without verification these recordings must remain in doubt. As Jupiter has such an interesting source of radio waves, we might expect the rather similar ones, Saturn, Uranus, and Neptune, to radiate also. Saturn is a likely looking candidate, with the similarity of its atmosphere to that of Jupiter and with those spectacular and quite magical rings round it we feel we could expect almost anything from it. But according to results so far, we must regard Jupiter as an exception, and we must hope that its radiations are no mere temporary phenomenon which will fade and be lost like other surface features. Even the great Red Spot is only eighty years old, and when so little is known about the appearance and disappearance of such large markings we may one day find ourselves lamenting the loss of the only known 20 Mc/s cosmical pulse transmitter.

Radar Echoes from the Planets

The success of moon radar and the building of new large radio telescopes have turned attention towards the extremely difficult technical problem of obtaining radar echoes from the planets. The size of the nearer planets and their least distances from the earth are compared with the moon in the Table. The last column gives a measure of the improvement in performance required over that necessary for obtaining an echo from the moon, assuming that

	Distance (miles)	Diameter (miles)	Required sensitivity
Moon	240,000	2,200	1
Venus	23 million	7,700	5 million
Mars	33 million	4,200	80 million
Mercury	48 million	3,100	600 million
Jupiter	360 million	89,000	3,000 million

the planet reflects as well as the moon. Formidable as the lowest factor of 5 million may seem, it is not quite out of the question to obtain echoes from Venus. At Jodrell Bank a very powerful transmitter has been constructed for sending pulses to Venus, and a sensitive and complex receiver is used for detecting echoes. Large Doppler frequency shifts are to be expected, and the receiver must allow for these. Long averaging times are used, just as Bay in Hungary only obtained definite evidence of moon echoes after half an hour of averaging. The experiment is also being carried out by the Lincoln Laboratory in Massachusetts; both laboratories now report the successful reception of Venus echoes. The Lincoln Laboratory was the first to achieve this *tour de force*.

Clear and systematic observations of echoes from Venus would be enormously useful in astronomy. As with the moon, the surface of the planet can be explored by measuring its reflection coefficient and by observing the fading of the echo. Observations of the rate of fading of the echo would solve the problem of the rate of rotation of Venus. On a different question, the radio pulse in its long journey, taking about four minutes altogether, would explore for us an unknown stretch of interplanetary space, and the condition in which it returns might tell us how many electrons it had encountered and what was the value of the magnetic field along its path. Finally, an exact timing of the four minutes' delay between transmission and reception would give a measure of the distance to Venus, and it might be sufficiently accurate to improve our measurements of distances inside the solar system and thereby to improve the basis of the whole scheme of measured astronomical distances. The first measurements of this distance, by the Lincoln Laboratory, have already given a result of the same accuracy as any previous optical method.

CHAPTER 16

Meteors and Comets

ON any starlight night the unchanging majesty of the heavens may be suddenly enhanced by the flashing trail of a meteor or shooting star. A patient observer may be rewarded by the sight of perhaps half a dozen in an hour; during a few nights of the year he may see over a hundred in an hour, and when this occurs we speak of the increased incidence of meteors as a 'meteor shower'. Meteors may be seen from all over the earth and are continually shooting into our atmosphere. In a single period of twenty-four hours there must be over a million meteors falling on the earth as a whole and over twenty million during meteor showers.

There are also many more fainter meteors, visible only with the aid of a telescope where their trails are often found crossing photographs of stars. Some of the largest meteors survive their passage through the air and fall to the earth as meteorites, the largest of all weighing some hundreds of tons. Some of the very smallest also fall to earth without burning up completely and can be found as a light meteoritic dust. In all, about ten tons of material are added to our planet every day, by the impact of meteors.

Fragments and dust from meteors and meteorites show that they are made from materials similar to those of which the earth is made, although there appear to be two distinct types of meteors, the stone and the iron varieties. The stone ones usually contain some iron, but on the whole their composition corresponds closely with the outer rocky parts of the earth; the iron meteorites contain up to 99 per cent of a nickel-iron alloy. Probably these correspond with the inner parts of the earth, which are known to be heavier, and to be magnetic. Here is our most tangible connexion with outer space; so close in fact that it was for a time considered that meteorites actually came from Earth, being shot out from volcanoes in prehistoric times.

Meteorites may be seen in many museums of Natural History. They range in size up to the 36-ton specimen from Cape York,

Greenland, now preserved in New York, and all of them have ended on the surface of our planet after a journey that aspiring space travellers might envy but could not hope to imitate. Where do they come from?

Considering that the origin of the solar system itself is an unsolved mystery, that of the meteors cannot be expected to be obvious. The question that must first be answered – and here radio astronomers have made an important contribution to meteor astronomy – is whether or not they belong to the solar system themselves. If they do not, do they permeate interstellar space throughout the galaxy? And if they do belong to the solar system, do they show the concentration to the plane of the ecliptic which is the most marked feature of the other members, planets, asteroids, and comets?

Comets and Showers

In searching for the origin of meteors we distinguish at the outset between the meteors arriving in showers and those of sporadic occurrence. Sporadic meteors have long been a puzzle, but the origin of the meteor showers has become quite clear since the discovery that they are closely associated with comets (Figure 39).

Comets which can only be observed in telescopes are quite common. The Comet Arend-Roland which appeared in 1955 was much more spectacular, and provided a world-wide spectacle equalling Halley's Comet, which last appeared in 1910. Comets such as these move rapidly across the sky, coming into sight as a faint diffuse point and developing the characteristic tail as they approach the sun. As they recede, after only a few days, the tail swings round so that it always points away from the sun, just as though the sun were continually blowing it away from itself.

The motion of a comet can be plotted with great accuracy, and an orbit can be computed just as for a planet. Most comets prove to lie in elliptical orbits, although the ellipse is often so elongated that the portion near the sun is very like a parabola. On a hyperbolic orbit, a comet would leave the solar system altogether, and it would then be a passing visitor, seen once only. A parabola is a 'borderline' orbit, with elliptical and hyperbolic orbits as general cases on either side. Cometary orbits go so far out from the sun that the period of return visits may extend to hundreds of years, and perhaps more, but many periods shorter than this are known. For the recurring comets, measurements of the orbit on one single passage often give a value for the period which is closely corroberated by successive visits of the comet. Halley's Comet is the prime example of this, with twenty-seven appearances at regular

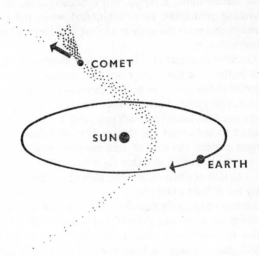

39. The origin of meteor showers. The earth in its orbit encounters a trail of debris following the orbit of a comet

intervals of seventy-seven years since 87 B.C. There are also several comets with a period of less than ten years, moving in much smaller orbits. These are believed to have been deflected from larger orbits by passing close to the massive planet Jupiter.

A passage close to the sun can have a disastrous effect on a comet. A comet seen in 1845 was one that had been seen on several occasions; in 1826 Biela had computed this orbit and shown that it had a period of 6½ years. On this occasion, however, it was seen to be accompanied by a small fellow-traveller, which appeared to grow in brightness through the passage of the comet, as if the head were breaking into two parts. The next return of Biela's comet, in 1852, was the last time it was seen, and it then consisted of two faint parts separated by over a million miles. On several subsequent periods it was looked for, and no comet was to be found at all, but the remains of the comet were quite clearly seen. At the appointed times of return, in 1872, 1885, 1892, and 1899, when the earth crossed the orbit of the vanished comet, there were spectacular meteor showers. Apparently the debris of the comet was still travelling round the same orbit, and when the earth passed through this orbit the shower of dust was observed as the Bielid Meteor shower.

Giacobini's comet also has a meteor shower, the Giacobinids, and in this case the shower does not merely represent a sort of afterlife of the comet, as both comet and meteor shower exist together. Our planet, Earth, crosses the Giacobini orbit at different distances from the comet each year, and it appears that when it is nearest to the comet the shower is most intense. Certainly the largest meteor showers of this century came during passages closest to the comet. Another shower, the Perseids, has the same orbit as that of a comet, and this shower has been recurring regularly for at least 1,000 years.

Meteor showers are therefore seen to be the results of collisions between the earth and the orbits of comets, orbits which contain either the stuff from which comets are made or the debris into which they disintegrate. Comets and meteors then constitute one problem together, which is a part of the general problem of the origin of the solar system.

Sporadic Meteors

It is one thing to determine the orbits of a group of some hundreds of meteors, all of which prove to be travelling along the same elliptical path, and quite another to determine the orbits of the few sporadic meteors seen every night. There is now no relation between successive meteors; they all travel in different directions. Computing orbits of individual meteors, appearing without warning in any part of the sky, would seem to be an almost impossible task, but it is one which has fascinated many astronomers, and much work has been done in this field. Professor Whipple in Harvard has done extensive work in photographing meteor tracks in such a way as to determine both the speed and direction of the meteor. In 1945 when Hey and Stewart first used radar methods for studying meteor trails, the difficulties in their study by photographic methods were still so great that no definite conclusions could be drawn. Some observers thought that no hyperbolic orbits were to be found, others that all sporadic meteors had hyperbolic orbits and came, not from our own solar system, but from the remote spaces between the stars. Radio astronomy, or rather 'radar astronomy', has now firmly settled this controversy.

Radar Echoes and Meteor Trails

When a meteor strikes the atmosphere it may have any velocity between about five and fifty miles per second. Encounters between atmospheric gas and a meteor result in a slowing down of the meteor and also in the heating which makes it glow visibly. The trail of such encounters is a trail of ionized gas, which diffuses away and recombines over a period of some seconds. This trail reflects radio waves. The details of this reflection have been investigated for a number of years, and two types have been found. Around the meteor itself is a head of dense ionization, which can produce its own echo. The long trail acts separately from the head, and as far as long radio waves are concerned it looks like a long thin piece of conducting wire stretched across the sky. Such a piece of wire reflects radio waves back upon their own path when the waves are reflected perpendicularly to the wire, at 'normal incidence'.

This second type of reflection was the first to be demonstrated and understood. In 1945 Hey and Stewart, working in the Army Operational Research Group, arranged three radar sets using the same long wavelength all to search simultaneously for meteors in one patch of sky. The radars were situated many miles apart, at Richmond, at Walmer, and at Aldeburgh, so that this small patch of sky, at a height of about sixty miles, was being examined from three different directions. Each radar received over 2,000 meteor echoes during the six weeks of observations, but only on four occasions was the same trail observed by two sets simultaneously. Each radar was selecting only those meteor trails which crossed the beam at right angles.

During a meteor shower the same three radars showed an echo rate which reached a peak at different times, when the shower was cutting perpendicularly through the separate aerial beams; these times gave a measure of the direction of the shower, or its 'radiant'. It was now possible to measure the radiant of a shower without a single meteor being seen, and further, it was now possible to measure the radiants of meteor showers falling on the earth in daylight hours. Hey and Stewart in fact showed in the same year that there were important showers, to be observed only by radio methods, through many summer days, although it was the work of Professor Lovell and his colleagues at Jodrell Bank which gave the first clear description of these daytime showers.

In October 1946 several different teams were already at work on meteor echoes. At Jodrell Bank the new radio observatory was making a modest beginning with one mobile radar set in a trailer. Appleton and Naismith at the D.S.I.R. research station at Slough, and new research teams in America, were all preparing to join with Hey in observations of the meteor showers expected when the earth crossed the orbit of the Giacobini comet on 9–10 October. A prolific meteor shower was expected at this time, but the number of echoes observed was far greater than ever was hoped. The sporadic rate of echoes on one particular equipment was about two per hour: this was observed up to the time of the expected shower when the rate jumped up to 200 per minute, rising to this very high rate and falling again in only six hours. From that time onwards radar astronomy was an established science, with all kinds of new techniques rapidly being added to the straightforward military radar sets. New results poured out at a pace which seemed to be limited only by the speed of the earth's passage through successive meteor showers.

Meteor Velocities

The elucidation of the origin of the sporadic meteors depended on the measurement of their velocity. There are now several ways of measuring this velocity: the most obvious apply to the type of echo which comes from the head of ionization rather than from the trail itself. This head can be observed as a moving echo, like the radar echo from an aircraft, and the velocity can be measured either from the rate at which its range changes with time, or, more directly, from a measurement of Doppler shift in the echo. Strangely enough, the echoes from the line trail can also give a measurement of velocity, from a peculiar variation of the echo as the trail grows in length. These variations are shown in Plate 11A. Diffraction theory must be used to explain them; fortunately the precise theory was already available, having been formulated by Fresnel for light waves in 1816. According to Fresnel's diffraction theory, the echo builds steadily up to half its final value at the time when the meteor crosses the foot of the perpendicular from the radar set to the meteor trail. When the trail has crossed this point, oscillations of echo amplitude occur as the path length to the meteor increases by successive increments of one wavelength.

In 1947, 1948, and 1949, successful velocity determinations were made for the Geminid meteor showers by this diffraction technique, at Jodrell Bank. A velocity of $22\frac{1}{2}$ miles per second had already been found for several meteors of this shower by Whipple, and the radar measurements gave precisely the same result. Now the radar measurements could be used to tackle the unsolved and burning question of the sporadic meteors.

When a meteor is encountered by the earth travelling in its orbit round the sun, the actual velocity with which the meteor enters the earth's atmosphere depends on the relation between the meteor orbit and the earth's orbit. If the meteor is met head-on, for example, the velocity may be three times that of a meteor which is overtaking the earth in its orbit. For each direction there is, however, a critical velocity which represents a border line between theories, with higher velocities belonging only to meteors which must have travelled in hyperbolic orbits, entering the solar system from outside.

The idea of encountering meteors from outside our solar system is one that excites the imagination, and many experiments

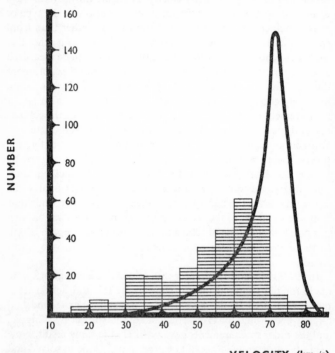

VELOCITY (km./s)

40. The measured velocities of meteors. The fill-line curve gives the expected distribution of velocities if all meteors have the energy required to escape from the solar system. The 'histogram' of observed velocities shows that meteors all have energies lower than this limit

have now been performed to search for such high-velocity visitors. It is perhaps rather disappointing that few have been found which can even be suspected of such a wild journey. Figure 40 shows the result of one search, when the meteors arriving 'head-on' to the earth's motion were being investigated by Davies and Lovell at Jodrell Bank. The smooth curve shows the distribution of velocities to be expected if the sporadic meteors were all travelling at the limiting velocity of a parabolic orbit, and it is evident that the actual velocities are well below this limit. Sporadic meteors arriving from many directions have also been investigated by McKinley in Canada, and all observatories agree that practically all these meteors belong to our solar system. Further, it is becoming clear that many of these meteors move in orbits rather similar to those of the planets, and it begins to seem rather that sporadic meteors are closely related to the asteroids, the group of tiny planets, some no more than a few miles across, which occupy the space between Mars and Jupiter. It may be that the smallest asteroids are just the same bodies as the largest meteorites, and that all are in fact simply planets, with a continuous gradation in size. But to establish the exact relation between the various small members of the solar system, comets, meteors, and asteroids, we need to know more about the distribution of the sporadic meteors in space. This is now the main subject of meteor research. The most puzzling feature of the distribution is the appearance of some meteor orbits inclined at large angles to the plane of the ecliptic; the planets and asteroids are so closely confined to the ecliptic that it is hard to find any dynamic reason for this departure.

With meteors, asteroids, and planets forming such a diverse collection of objects travelling in the suns gravitational field, it is interesting to speculate whether the smaller bodies are planets in the making or planets in a stage of dissolution. In fact which came first, the planets or the meteors, or does the process work both ways? There is so much detailed evidence that must be taken into account by any theoretical explanation of the planetary system that any theory becomes liable to severe criticism. The only theories which approach a convincing explanation propound that the planets condensed out of the same nebular material as the sun, and they suggest that the formation of planets of all sizes would be a natural occurrence in this process. This would mean that the meteors and asteroids represent condensations which never achieved sufficient size to grow to a true planet.

It cannot be said that any theory so far offers precise information about the development of our solar system. When we come to a better understanding of this process we shall be better able to assess the position of humanity in the Universe. For if other stars tend naturally to acquire planetary systems of their own, invisible to us because so very much more distant than our sun, then planets must exist in such vast numbers that the probability of life developing in the warmth of other suns is no longer remote.

The Arend–Roland Comet

It was exciting to hear in 1955 that another bright comet was on its way towards us, after a gap of forty-five years since 1910, when both Halley's comet and another equally bright one were seen. Radio astronomers were among those who made preparations to observe anything they could of this rare phenomenon, since little is known of the physical conditions in comets and their tails. The fact that they were able to add very little to this knowledge should be admitted at the outset, but their investigations were nevertheless both worthy and worthwhile.

The head of a comet usually contains a bright nucleus, which is the only really substantial part. This is probably a loose agglomeration of meteoritic material. Around it is a diffuse gaseous envelope called the coma, and this draws out into a long tenuous tail which grows as the comet approaches the sun. The tail is so insubstantial that it is blown away from the comet head by the mere pressure of sunlight, so that the comet always appears to be pointing towards the sun. The light from the comet is reflected sunlight. Faint spectral lines in it indicate that it contains molecular material with low atomic weights.

The radio astronomers who were joining in the observations of Comet Arend–Roland (named after the Belgian astronomers who first discovered it) had to ask themselves what radio studies could best contribute to our understanding of the comet. Their studies would be limited to about two weeks of observations and careful preparation was necessary to make the best use for such a limited time for experiment and observation.

Certainly the head would be no more accessible by radio astronomy than are the asteroids or the more distant planets, but the tail might well contain ionized gas in sufficient quantity for appreciable refraction of radio waves, and it might even radiate at radio wavelengths if there were enough electrons at a high enough temperature. Two kinds of experiments were planned therefore: one to detect direct radiation from any part of the comet, and the second to examine radio waves from more distant sources when they traversed the comet's trail.

Radio telescopes of all kinds were trained on the comet during the week of its closest approach. There were several reports of radio waves emitted from the tail, but there were very many more which stated categorically that nothing detectable was emitted over a wide range of frequencies. Only one positive report remains, claiming that radiation was received on 600 Mc/s, using a 27-ft parabolic reflector. In the face of the many negative reports this had to be considered as doubtful, and the explanation that a 600-Mc/s emission was a radio spectral line emission cannot easily be accepted. The search for direct radiation was therefore inconclusive; we shall need another similar comet to experiment with before there can be any conviction that comets or their tails radiate at all.

As for the refraction measurements, these proved also to be rather disappointing. Few radio telescopes were available to work at the low frequencies required, and only one experiment was performed. Whitfield at Cambridge, with his 38-Mc/s radio-star interferometer was unable to show any evidence of refraction, so that the sum total of radio observations of the comet gave it a very poor radio performance. Whitfield's results could be interpreted as showing that there must be less than 10^4 electrons per cc. in the comet's tail – but it would have been surprising to find that amount anyway.

It might appear that radio astronomers were wasting their time in looking at so unpromising an object. But when the question is asked 'Do comets radiate directly, or can they refract radio waves?', the answer 'no' is just as much an answer as a more positive one, and an inconclusive result makes us seek further evidence when another opportunity arises. It can hardly be stated as scientific fact, but sometimes it would seem that the radio significance of celestial objects is inversely proportional to their optical impression – and the Arend–Roland comet certainly was no disappointment optically.

CHAPTER 17

The Ionosphere

IT is now thirty-five years since the terrestrial ionosphere was discovered by Appleton and Barnett, and during these years there has been continuous research into its composition. The practical importance of the ionosphere lies, of course, in its property of reflecting radio waves in the broadcast band, allowing shortwave communication to be carried out on a world-wide scale. The ionosphere is, however, a difficult object to study, for it is very complicated in its structure and, further, it changes its structure in a complicated way. Standard ionospheric sounding by radar techniques has provided most of our present knowledge of the electron density, but only for the lower part of the ionosphere. Radio waves which have penetrated past the region of maximum electron density never return, and no radar information is available apart from a few scattered indications of irregularities in the upper part of the F-region. It is hardly unfair to the painstaking and detailed work of that thirty-five years to say that it has revealed many more unanswered problems than the considerable number of problems which have actually been solved. To the radio astronomer the ionosphere has a nuisance value only, since it may distort his view of the radio sources beyond; the radio physicist has, however, found these distortions of great interest in his study of the ionosphere.

The conventional picture of the ionosphere is of a sheet of ionized gas about 100 miles above the surface of the earth, with a density of electrons varying according to the sunlight falling upon it. This sheet is extended in height and maximum density is found in it at two separate heights, about 90 miles (E-region) and 200 miles (F-region). The F-region contains a greater density than the E-region, and it also extends through a greater range of heights. Beyond this, the description becomes more complex. A D-region is now recognized, which occurs just below the E-region; this D-region reflects the very longest radio wavelengths used in communications. The F-region is split into two layers, the F_1- and F_2-regions. Each of these layers is traversed by the earth's magnetic field and consequently reflects radio waves in complex ways depending on their polarization. But the main trouble about the ionosphere is that this simple picture, drawn in terms of definite smooth layers which only change slowly through the day, is overcome by the most violent changeability and by such drastic departures from smoothness that its description comes to resemble the complexity of meteorology.

Conventional radar reflections from the E-region are fairly easily interpreted. They show how the ionization increases smoothly with height, and they enable us to estimate the temperature and pressure of the atmosphere at heights only occasionally reached by rockets and satellites. When a solar flare occurs, the change in reflection shows that the increase in ultra-violet light from the sun has given a corresponding increase in ionization at the lowest levels, and all the changes here may be followed in detail. Reflections of shorter radio waves from greater heights are more difficult to interpret, as the waves have to traverse more complex patterns of ionization before they are reflected back, and they have then to traverse them again. The double effect becomes harder to interpret as the reflections occur from higher and higher levels. Finally, a point is reached where no reflection occurs at all and the ionosphere above is then inaccessible to these methods.

Radio astronomy has here a twofold advantage. Waves from a radio star pass right through the ionosphere, exploring it from top to bottom, and they only pass through once. For the upper region, that is for the F_2-region, the effects of ionization on these radio waves provide an invaluable new tool of exploration. As will be seen in the following accounts of the work already achieved, the radio transmitters on artificial satellites are providing new radio stars in the sky, which are particularly useful because they have so great a brightness compared with the natural ones.

Scintillation

When Hey was making his first survey of cosmic radio waves, he found that the radio signal from one direction in the constellation of Cygnus was fluctuating rapidly in strength. There was no indication of the cause, which might have been either a change in emission or an effect of the transmission path from the source. In either case the source had to be a relatively small object, possibly only a few minutes of arc across, and this was the consideration that enabled Hey to say he had discovered a 'radio star'. It was several years before the cause of the fluctuation was discovered, and it turned out then that the ionosphere was responsible. (The radio star itself, Cygnus A, is a quarter of a million light-years across, and an object of this size can hardly fluctuate in emission during a period of a few seconds.)

Scintillation is a familiar effect in optical astronomy. Most telescopes are at the bottom of the atmosphere, where any starlight which has traversed air without being actually absorbed has traversed turbulent irregularities, and been bent and diffracted in a series of random directions. As a result stellar images dance around and change their brightness, often so much that they appear even to the naked eye to twinkle, or 'scintillate'. A simple picture of this random refraction is given by the pattern of light on the bottom of a swimming pool, where ripples on the surface appear to focus light into ridges and blobs which move along the bottom of the pool as the ripples move along the surface. From beneath the surface a bright light will appear both to move about and to change its brightness as the ripples move past. The ionosphere contains blobs of ionization that act on radio waves just as these ripples act on light.

Proof of the ionospheric origin of scintillation was obtained by a cooperative experiment between Cambridge and Jodrell Bank observatories. Simultaneous recordings of radio waves from Cygnus A were made on the same wavelength at the two places, and it was found not only that individual fluctuations in brightness were quite unrelated but that occasionally no fluctuations at all were found at one place when they were strongly recorded at the other. A systematic investigation of scintillations, leading to a description of the ionospheric irregularities, was then undertaken by A. Hewish in Cambridge.

Hewish used two simultaneous recordings of the radio waves from a single radio star, enabling him to separate out the scintillation in intensity from the scintillation in direction. The significance of this separation is seen in Figure 41, where effects close to the irregularities are compared with those further away. Close to, only angular scintillation is observed, while the intensity scintillation builds up as the distance increases. The relation between

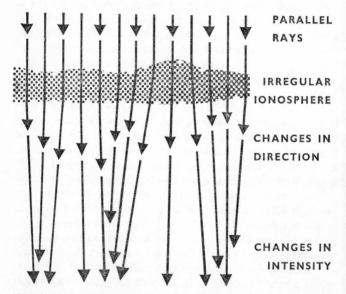

PARALLEL
RAYS

IRREGULAR
IONOSPHERE

CHANGES IN
DIRECTION

CHANGES IN
INTENSITY

41. Scintillation of a radio star. Diffraction of a 'rough' ionosphere causes firstly a scintillation in direction; further from the irregularities there will also be scintillation in intensity

the two scintillations can therefore be used to measure the height of the irregularities. Furthermore, the scale of the pattern of intensity on the ground can give the size of the blobs of ionization, just as the ripples of light demonstrate the size of the water ripples in the swimming pool. Finally, the movements of the blobs show as movements of the pattern, and this can be measured by following the changes of intensity at two points about a mile apart.

Radio scintillation is found to be a phenomenon of the lower part of the F-region, where it appears that blobs of ionization about three miles across, elongated along the earth's magnetic field, are to be found in a layer about 200 miles up. The pattern blows along, usually at speeds of about 100 m.p.h., but when an eruption on the sun has caused a magnetic storm the speed is greatly increased, sometimes to over 2,000 m.p.h.

As with many other details of the ionosphere, the cause of the irregularities is unknown. Two clues towards the answer are provided by the variation of the effect geographically and by its variation with time of day. On the whole, scintillation is to be seen at night-time rather than daytime, which argues against an origin in solar radiation. The only other irregular ionospheric pheno-

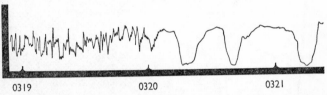

0319   0320   0321

42. Scintillation. The irregular fading of this 40 Mc/s record of Sputnik I between 0319 and 0320 shows that the satellite was passing through or behind the ionospheric irregularities that cause scintillation of radio stars

menon to be observed mainly at night is the Aurora, which admittedly can only actually be seen in the dark, but which shows little sign of continuing into daylight hours. Geographic variation of scintillation is not known in detail, although as far as the local variations within about 1,000 miles of Cambridge are concerned, the Russian satellites have provided some most interesting results.

When Sputnik I came near this country it was flying at heights which varied from about 150 miles to 300 miles, according to the part of the elliptical orbit which lay overhead at the time. The transmitters on 20 Mc/s and 40 Mc/s (wavelengths 15 and 7½ metres) were of a low enough frequency for their transmission to be greatly disturbed by the ionosphere if the satellite was above the blobby region; the irregularities in signal shown in the left half of Figure 42 are just the same fluctuations as the scintillations of a natural radio star. This transit was made at height of 300 miles. During the night of 13–14 October Sputnik I made a transit across Europe every hour and a half; tracks of these passages are shown in Figure 43. Marked along the tracks

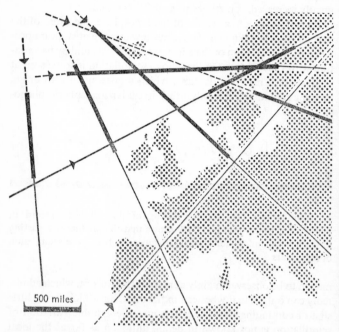

500 miles

43. Tracks of Sputnik I over Europe, 13–14 October 1957. The heavy lines show the portions of the tracks where scintillation of the radio signals was observed. No signals were received from the parts of the track shown with a broken line

are the positions of the satellite when scintillation was observed. A well-defined patch of disturbance, stretching at least 2,000 miles in longitude and extending 500 miles north of Scotland, can be seen, and the height of 200 miles can be found from the difference in behaviour of the low and high transits. This is a typical 'cloud' or irregularity, such as is often found north of this country, but not so often in the south. Again there is some resemblance to the distribution of the Aurora.

Scintillation is being used as a means of exploring the ionosphere, but to many radio astronomers this is as much a diversion of their attention as it would be for optical astronomers to turn their attention to the structure of the atmosphere. Scintillation is, in plain fact, a nuisance which prevents good observations of astronomical objects by radio waves of long wavelength. The radio astronomer suffers from 'bad seeing'. He may be forced to plan longwave observations for the time of sunspot minimum, when the skies are somewhat clearer of this and the other troubles now to be described.

Exploration by Refraction

At the instant when the sun sets below the horizon it appears to us that a straight line between the observer and the sun is just touching the horizon; in fact it goes well below the horizon, since the rays of light are bent by about half a degree by their passage through the air. The day is therefore several minutes longer than plain celestial geometry would suggest.

Radio waves are also bent by the atmosphere in just the same way as light, with two extra effects due respectively to water vapour and to the ionosphere. It is no great help to have another method of detecting water vapour, as it is usually found in the lower atmosphere where meteorology is well equipped with observations. But the ionosphere has long suffered from the difficulty of detailed observations, and when radio waves of fairly long wavelength are found to be refracted appreciably by the ionosphere it is possible to regard this as not merely a nuisance but as a means of exploration in itself.

For atmospheric refraction the angular deviation depends only on the density of the air at ground level, and on the altitude of the star being observed. Ionospheric refraction depends on the detailed distribution of electrons through the dense F-region, and the two refractions, as a ray enters and leaves the ionosphere, vary in a more complicated way with altitude. To work back from an observed deviation and obtain the distribution of ionization is difficult, and so far the method has not been found useful.

Another rather similar effect of the ionosphere has, however, been shown to be of some value. The ionization due to sunlight varies through the day according to the angle of elevation of the sun, so that at dawn or dusk the ionization above an observer will be in the form of a wedge, increasing in thickness in the direction from darkness to daylight. This wedge will deflect radio waves in an east-west direction, and the deflection measures the change of ionization.

Wedge refraction was observed for over a year by the author at Cambridge. A long series of measurements of the positions of four radio stars was in progress, at a time when the identities of none of them was certain and it was thought possible that real movements might be detected. The absurdity of such an experiment is now made evident by the very large known distances of the radio stars, but the rather incidental measurement of ionospheric refraction turned out better than expected. It was in fact the first observation of the ionosphere which included the upper regions above the maximum of the F-region, and it provided the first measurement of the relation of the total number of electrons in the whole ionosphere to the number up to that point. The upper part was found to contain about 2/3 of the total ionization, a proportion confirmed by later experiments.

Faraday Rotation

A more potent probe for this exploration of the upper ionosphere is now provided by the radar echoes from the moon. The ionosphere has another effect on radio waves besides deflecting them: it changes their polarization. Any radio aerial transmits a polarized wave, as for example the vertical polarization of the B.B.C. Television services, and the horizontal polarization of the V.H.F. sound broadcasts. Michael Faraday showed that the plane of polarization of light is rotated when it passes through a block of glass with a magnetic field aligned along the path of the light: in the same way, the plane of polarization of a radar pulse travelling through the ionosphere is rotated by the combined effect of the ionization and the earth's magnetic field, and when it returns from the moon it is rotated again by the same amount. The total rotation gives a very direct measurement of the total ionization, and, furthermore, it is a comparatively easy quantity to measure. For example the Jodrell Bank experimental moon echoes at 120 Mc/s suffered five rotations on the way to the moon and back, from which it may be deduced that there were no less than five million million electrons in each square centimetre column of the ionosphere at this time. This most exact measurement will certainly be the basis of much ionospheric sounding, but it does not of course provide any information on the distribution of density with height. It would be useful if a reflector, or a transmitter, could be placed at various heights successively for the successive exploration of different levels. Extravagant as this demand may seem, it has been met by the advent of the artificial satellite, which has already been mentioned as an explorer of the scintillating F-region.

The Satellite as Explorer of the Ionosphere

At 9 a.m. on 5 October 1957, the Radio Astronomy Group at the Cavendish Laboratory sat down to their usual Saturday morning discussion. The news of the successful launching of the first artificial satellite, Sputnik I, had just been received, and the whole group expressed their admiration and wonder at what had been achieved. Along with the sense of admiration came a desire to join in with this great enterprise in some small way, and it occurred to several members that the Cavendish Laboratory's radio telescopes were easily adaptable to record the radio signals being transmitted on 20 Mc/s and 40 Mc/s. Furthermore, it was evident that most of the world was so taken aback by Sputnik I that very few laboratories outside the U.S.S.R. would be ready to make such recordings and that vital information on the track of the satellite might be completely lost.

With great enthusiasm and with makeshift alterations to existing equipment, observations were started on that same night. For the next week few members of the group had any sleep, as the satellite passed over England several times during each night, while each day was spent in computation and in building or adapting apparatus for the next night's work.

For the first week the main concern was to plot the track of the satellite from its radio signals, and it was soon found possible to predict its track across the country to an accuracy of about ten miles. The Cavendish Laboratory achieved the distinction of being the first to publish accurate details of the satellite's orbit, with measured changes in the orbit due to precession and air resistance. But after this had been superseded by more accurate visual tracking, the radio results were looked at again for any help they might give in ionospheric exploration.

As has been described already, scintillation could clearly be seen on the recordings, providing a greatly improved method of exploring irregularities in the F-region. But the most prominent effect was a periodic variation in signal, seen on practically every recording. This was at first supposed to be an indication that the satellite was rotating, so that its aerial was seen periodically from different directions. Then it was noticed that different speeds of fading were being recorded on the different frequencies, and it was clear that Faraday rotation was the chief cause. As the satellite moved across the sky it was usually climbing or falling at a rate of several hundred miles an hour, depending on its elliptical orbit, and the line of sight was therefore including a rapidly varying amount of ionosphere. The same rotation observed for the moon echoes was now being observed for the one-way transmission from the satellite, and the possibility of counting electrons in the ionosphere was at once demonstrated. Further, an actual rotation of the satellite was eventually found, and it was possible to study both the speed of this rotation and the direction of its axis.

This new era in ionospheric exploration is perhaps too young for a true assessment of its value to be made. It has already been found that the 20 Mc/s and 40 Mc/s transmissions of the Sputniks are very much affected by the ionosphere, perhaps too much for an easy interpretation of the various effects of refraction and scintillation, and work on higher frequencies may be necessary. The transmitters on early satellites were not there primarily for propagation research, but to relay information from other apparatus. Planned experiments which use transmitters of chosen frequency flown at chosen heights are yet to come, but they are needed before full advantage can be made of the great opportunities of this exciting new era.

Satellite Navigation

There is a reverse side to the newly struck coin of satellite tracking. The efforts which have gone into accurate radio measurements and timings of the transits of a satellite have been directed

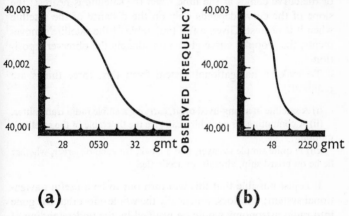

(a)   (b)

44. Doppler frequency shifts observed on Sputnik I, 9 October 1957. At 05.30 G.M.T. the satellite passed at a range of 650 km., giving the frequency change (a). At 22.48 G.M.T. the satellite passed nearly overhead, at a range of 250 km. (b)

towards finding an unknown orbit from a known position on earth. What if we do not know where we are on earth, but a satellite is passing nearly overhead on an orbit which has previously been established? Can the radio transmissions from the satellite be used to find our own position, with the successive tracks of the satellite laying down a navigational grid covering the whole world? If this could be done, the world would for the first time be provided with a radio navigational aid which would be accurate over the whole globe to about five miles, which compares favourably with the accuracy of conventional astronavigation, The irregularities of the ionosphere would have no effect, provided that a high enough frequency were used.

The simplest way of tracking satellites by radio has been found to be by watching the frequency of the radio signal as the satellite passes over. Two records of the apparent frequency of the transmitter in Sputnik I are seen in Figure 44. The change in frequency is the result of the Doppler effect, and it drops in the same way that the note of a jet aircraft drops as it flies overhead. The centre of the curve comes at the time when the satellite is nearest: the slope of the curve depends only on the distance of the satellite when it is nearest. Given a full time-table of the satellite's movements, the Doppler curve gives immediately the observer's position.

To make a navigational system from this, three things are required:

(i) A satellite in a long-lived orbit, carrying a stable radio transmitter.

(ii) A computing service which can give the timetable of the satellite's motion.

(iii) A quite simple receiver, and a clock, for each observer, whether he be on board ship, aircraft, or arctic sledge.

It is just possible that this will turn out to be a useful navigational system; if it does, practically the whole effort that has gone into radio astronomy would be justified by the understanding of radio direction finding that has come from measurements of radio stars. Fundamental science in fact needs no such justification, but an unexpected practical bonus is always welcome.

CHAPTER 18

Radio Telescopes

THE survey of the radio universe has now been followed in the preceding chapters from the sun out to the edge of space and time, and back through the planets and the moon to the terrestrial ionosphere. We now return to the instruments with which this exploration has been carried out. What are the radio eyes and radio telescopes which have so greatly extended our view of the universe?

The range of wavelengths of light which can be appreciated by the human eye lies in the centre of the range which penetrates the terrestrial atmosphere. On either side of this visible spectrum lie the ultra-violet and infra-red regions, which are not greatly absorbed by the atmosphere. In these regions the use of photographic methods allows a considerable extension of astronomical observation, by techniques which closely correspond to normal vision. It is not impossible to imagine the actual extension of normal vision into the ultra-violet and infra-red ranges by some biological development, though this would be a much more complicated matter than, for example, the extension of the audible spectrum of sound to include the high frequencies of sound waves used by many animals smaller than ourselves.

The development of human eyes for the reception of radio waves, which penetrate the atmosphere equally well, is, however, quite inconceivable. It is not impossible to find suitable refracting materials in nature: paraffin wax, for example can be used for making lenses for radio waves though it could hardly be considered an ideal material for eyes. The construction of a retina or other sensitive element is also hard to imagine. But the real difficulty lies in the much longer wavelengths of the radio spectrum, which make the accommodation of a directive aerial array, or antenna, a difficult problem. In fact, in any reasonably sized animal the aerial system would probably determine the appearance of the animal to the exclusion of all other features.

213

The evolution of eyes sensitive to light is marvellous indeed, but our blindness to radio waves is entirely reasonable. We have then to rely on our man-made aids to vision, the radio telescopes, if we are to take advantage of the radio window to the universe.

The history of astronomy begins with a long introductory era of observations unaided by any sort of telescope. In those early years astronomical instruments were all devices concerned entirely with the measurements of the positions of heavenly bodies, and with time. All over the world the remains of observatories belonging to ancient civilizations remind us of the importance of systematic observations, directed usually towards the magic of astrology or the necessities of navigation. The classical peak to which pre-telescopic astronomy attained is found in the work of Tycho Brahe, the Danish astronomer of the seventeenth century. His records of the movements of the planets allowed Kepler to formulate general laws governing the movements of planets around the sun. Both Tycho Brahe and Kepler also had the distinction of observing supernova explosions, and the remains of both these are now radio stars. (See Chapter 9.)

The use of telescopes enabled this positional type of observation to be made with much greater accuracy, and at the same time it opened the way for a less mechanistic and more physical approach in astronomy.

Radio astronomy has no 'naked eye' stage of observations. From its earliest beginnings it has depended on radio telescopes, and the approach, all along, has been entirely physical. The development of radio astronomy, and that of its necessary instruments the radio telescopes, has not been determined by practical requirements of navigation or the dictates of those who determine 'what the stars foretell'. It is true that the new science can be of some aid in the new navigational problems of space travelling objects; the Astronomer Royal has put this into perspective by his dictum 'Space travel is bilge'. And as for any concern with astrology, we have yet to see a horoscope cast with the aid of the radio stars.

Positional work has nevertheless been of great concern in the early work in radio astronomy, and, in this field, with the difficulty of the longer wavelengths to contend with, we find ourselves now about equal with Tycho Brahe in the accuracy we are able to attain. Accuracy is just about sufficient for most problems of identifying radio stars; but this attainment has come only after the development of a series of radio telescopes specifically built for positional work.

Side by side with position finding in radio astronomy has gone the development of radio telescopes of great sensitivity. Here the criterion is 'the bigger the better'. The first radio telescope, made by Reber, was designed solely for great sensitivity, just to see what could be seen in the sky. In Reber's maps can be seen the first delineation of the radio waves from the Milky Way, and also some unresolved patches which later were shown to be radio stars. From Reber's radio telescope derives a line of radio telescopes with increasing sensitivity, some designed to see as many radio stars as possible, and others for more general purposes.

It is impossible to separate radio telescopes into strict categories of sensitive and position-finding instruments, but there is a broad distinction between the two types. The distinction has led to quite different techniques of construction, each chosen for a specific experimental purpose. This deliberate choice of a particular construction for a particular experiment has meant that many of the notable radio telescopes of the last decade are already obsolete, with their experimental purpose fulfilled; no single radio telescope can ever claim to be a truly general-purpose instrument. Some of the large new radio telescopes have much greater versatility than earlier constructions, but it is recognized that they are still limited in their range of use. Versatility implies simplicity, and the parabolic reflectors, which are the simplest and the nearest approach to general purpose instruments, will therefore be described first. Interferometers of increasing complexity follow, leaving the actual radio receivers for separate treatment in a further chapter. This order is analogous to dividing the subject of optical telescopes into sections on large reflectors, on spectroscopes, and on photographic plates.

Parabolic Reflectors

The parabolic reflector of an electric fire receives heat from the element at its focus and reflects it forward over a wide area. The problem of detecting radio waves from a point in the sky is the opposite problem of collecting the radiation falling on as large an area as possible, and concentrating it at one place so that it can be fed into a radio receiver, amplified, and recorded. A parabolic reflector with a receiving aerial at its focus lends itself perfectly to this problem.

The 200-in. diameter optical telescope on Mt Palomar is built round a parabolic mirror which collects light falling on an area of 200 square feet and concentrates it on a photographic plate at the focus. This 200-in. mirror could also be used for collecting radio waves, but it would be a rather wasteful use of so accurate a surface. This surface is true to a fraction of a wavelength of light, and this is about a million times as good as it need be for radio waves. The parabolic 'mirror' used for collecting and focusing radio waves can be much larger than the 200 inches of the optical instrument, according to the wavelength of the radiation it is to receive, and can be made of sheet metal or a mesh of metal and wire, accurate to about a tenth of the wavelength concerned.

Apart from the obvious differences in construction and precision of surface between the optical and the radio telescope, there is an important difference in the arrangements at the focus. An optical telescope forms images of all stars within a considerable field of view, whereas a radio telescope has only a single pick-up for radio waves, at the exact focus of the parabola. The information about the sky comes not as a picture or a map, but as a voltage; furthermore this voltage represents not the radiation from one single direction but rather the average over a whole range of directions determined by the resolving power of the telescope.

Plates 12 and 13 show parabolic reflector radio telescopes of various sizes. So many of these 'dishes' are now in use throughout the world that it is impossible to show more than a representative selection; however, it is not only the numbers but the size which is increasing. In fact it would seem that however large a parabolic aerial a radio astronomer has available, he always has good reasons for wishing it even larger.

The 'resolving power' of a telescope is the measure of its ability to distinguish two sources of radiation separated by a small angular distance, and may be loosely defined as the minimum angular distance at which this is possible. It is also to be thought of as the angular beam-width of the telescope, and its value is determined by the ratio of the telescope aperature to the wavelength. For example, the 200-in. telescope has an optical resolving power of about 1/10th second of arc; the 250-ft Jodrell Bank radio telescope has a resolving power of one degree for a radio wavelength of one metre. The need for very large apertures in radio telescopes hardly needs emphasizing. Resolving power for the astronomer determines the fineness of the brush which he can use to paint his picture of the sky.

The construction of large parabolic radio telescopes presents considerable engineering problems. The reflecting surface of some large ones has been made immobile, a very economical expedient but one which limits the usefulness of the telescope. We will consider the fixed and moveable reflectors separately, although some of the design problems are common to both.

Steerable Parabolic Reflectors

The engineering problem here is simply stated. A large surface, accurately constructed out of sheet metal or wire mesh, has to be maintained in its correct shape while it is directed at any desired part of the sky. The distortions which must occur as it moves, and even when a moderate wind blows on its surface, must be kept down to less than one tenth of the shortest wavelength for which the reflector is used. However stiff the structure that holds the surface in place, it will bend under its own weight, and design has to stop at the point where extra stiffening adds further weight, which itself adds further distortion.

The Table lists some of the outstanding parabolic reflectors so far built, giving their diameters and the smallest wavelength for which they can be used with full resolving power. At shorter wavelengths they are still useable although with reduced efficiency. Part of the versatility of the large parabolic reflector as compared with other large radio telescopes lies in the ease with which the wavelength of operation can be altered. They are, however, more likely to be used at the shortest possible wavelength, determined by the precision of the structure.

Beyond the general level of performance represented by these

Location	Diameter	Shortest wavelength for full efficiency	Beamwidth at shortest wavelength
Jodrell Bank	250 ft	30 cm.	15' arc
Green Bank, U.S.A. (National Radio Obs.)	140 ft	3 cm.	2' arc
Maryland Point, U.S.A. (Naval Res. Lab.)	85 ft	3 cm.	5' arc
Dwingeloo, Leiden, Holland	85 ft	10 cm.	15' arc
Washington (Nav. Res. Lab.)	50 ft	8 mm.	2' arc

instruments it seems difficult to go without considerable changes of design. Two lines are possible; the first aimed at reducing the distortions, the second at reducing their effects on the actual reflecting surface.

The sketch (Figure 45) shows the conventional ways of mounting large paraboloid radio telescopes. All but the largest are put on a 'polar mount', and quite usually this has been achieved with supports close together, near the centre of the bowl. This follows the practice of optical instruments, and eases the problem of driving and controlling the telescope to point at any object in the sky. The 250-ft telescope is mounted from towers at either edge, so that steering is achieved by an elevation movement about an axis between the towers, and an azimuthal movement by a movement of the towers round a circular railway track. This form of mounting is called the 'alt-azimuth' mount. The use of two supports, together with further stiffening by the semi-circular arc slung beneath the bowl, considerably reduces the problem of support and has suggested the first measure towards increasing size, shown also in the sketch. This is simply a method of providing more supports, spreading the load more widely, and keeping unsupported spans to the minimum.

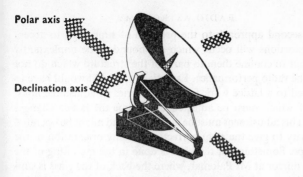

Polar axis

Declination axis

A

Elevation axis

B

Circular rail track
(azimuth movement)

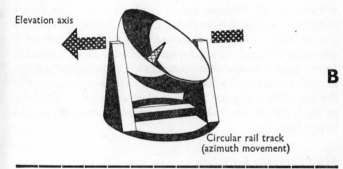

C

Load distributed over
several bearing circles

Concentric rails tracks

45. The mountings of paraboloid radio telescopes: (A) polar mount;
(B) altitude-azimuth mount; (C) possible mount for a very large paraboloid.

The second approach to the problem of support is to accept that distortions will occur which are bound to be unpleasantly large, but to confine them to parts of the structure which do not affect the radio performance. Essentially the bowl would have to be joined to a lattice work frame by a series of adjustable links, each of which must be adjusted every time the lattice changes shape. This adjustment must be automatic, and might be operated by gravity to give the right correction for any orientation of the telescope. Something of the kind is done in the mounting of the 200-in. mirror at Mt Palomar, where the back of the glass is supported in several different places by pads whose pressures vary with the orientation of the telescope.

Larger parabolic reflectors than the Jodrell Bank instrument will undoubtedly be made, and in fact there is already a design completed for a 600-ft reflector in the U.S.A. It is hard to envisage a much larger steerable paraboloid than this, but whatever is ultimately achieved, the step forward which the 250-ft reflector at Jodrell Bank represents must remain as one of the most significant in radio astronomy. The largest steerable reflector in existence at the time of its design was 50 feet in diameter; even the problems to which the new instrument is being applied were hardly defined at that time.

Fixed Parabolic Reflectors

There is a second large parabolic reflector also at Jodrell Bank, built in its original form in 1947 and measuring 225 feet in diameter. Lying on its back, it looks directly up at the zenith; its beam can only be moved a few degrees when the dipole aerial at the focus is moved sideways. A paraboloid lying on its back is very much cheaper than a paraboloid mounted on towers, which can be pointed anywhere in the sky. There may well be more of these fixed paraboloids built in sizes which cannot be attained by completely steerable instruments. There is already another 250-ft bowl, used by the Naval Research Laboratory in Washington for moon radar; this is an example of simplicity of construction, as it is made by bulldozing a carefully shaped hole out of the ground, and paving it with asphalt road surfacing. The shape is right to an accuracy of 3 inches, which is nearly as good as the Jodrell Bank steerable telescope, and though limited in use the great reduction in cost is commensurate with this limitation.

These fixed paraboloids cannot be classed among the versatile radio telescopes, but they are very well adapted to some particular experimental tasks. If directed at one part of the sky for a particular experiment it does not matter that a large part of the sky can never be seen by it. For example, in the Crimea the Lebedev Institute is studying the radio waves from the Crab nebula. They have therefore built a fixed parabolic reflector pointing at the right distance from the zenith, 100 feet in diameter and so accurately constructed that it works well at a wavelength of 10 cm.

To build larger versions of these fixed paraboloids may seem straightforward, but the engineering difficulties are not negligible. A tall tower must be built to hold the dipole feed at the focus, and this tower has to tilt if the beam is to be moveable. Designs which avoid this necessity of a tower at the focus have been proposed; in these the paraboloid is turned on its side, so that the axis runs nearly along the ground, and only the part of the reflecting surface above ground is built. The beam then is directed towards the horizon, but can be tilted either by tilting the reflector, or by moving the feed vertically, or even by using a second large reflecting surface which can tilt but is flat and easier to handle than the main reflector. Examples of these have been constructed at Pulkova and at Ohio State University (see Chapter 20).

Interferometers

Let us suppose that radio telescopes can be bought by the square yard, for a price which is not affected by their shape; and let us suppose that a radio astronomer has bought a certain number of square yards of collecting surface. What shape should he construct in order to obtain the best value for his expenditure?

One fairly obvious answer is to put it all inside a circular aperture, like the parabolic reflector; this gives a 'pencil beam' aerial, which receives radio waves from a comparatively small area of sky. But for some experiments it is advantageous to divide the total area up into two or more small parts and separate them from one another. The radio telescope then becomes an interferometer, which as we have already seen (Chapter 12) has a greater angular accuracy for position finding and may be used for distinguishing small objects against an intense background. A given area of collecting surface connotes a definite sensitivity; all that is changed by changing the shape is the reaction of the telescope to the angular structure of the radio sky.

An optical interferometer was made in 1923 by Michelson, who adapted the Mt Wilson 100-in. telescope for measuring the diameter of stars by dividing the telescope aperture with a system of mirrors. Correspondingly the radio interferometers using two aerials are often called Michelson interferometers, and their first use was to measure the diameters of radio stars, and of the radio sun.

The first Michelson radio interferometer was made by Ryle and Vonberg in Cambridge in 1946, and it was used to measure the diameter of an emitting sunspot. This interferometer used two aerials, each consisting of five dipoles mounted over a sheet of wire netting. Much larger aerials are now used for the weaker signals from radio stars, but the principle of the interferometer is the same in both applications.

Michelson had already pointed out the possibility of achieving more than a simple measurement of the diameter of a star, and had shown that the whole distribution of brightness over its surface was in principle measureable by an interferometer, provided that the separation between the two components could be varied. The limit of resolving power is set only by the maximum separation of the two mirrors, or aerials, and not by their actual size. By his arrangement of two small mirrors Michelson was able to attain with the 100-in. telescope a resolving power considerably better than that of the 200-in. telescope. But angular resolution is not the only advantage of interferometers. In recording weak radio stars, one difficulty of a single pencil beam aerial is the strength of the background of galactic radio emission. An interferometer can be used to reject this background and observe only sources with a small angular size, giving a greatly increased contrast in the recordings. Figure 46 shows some recordings made with an early radio star interferometer where this principle was first used; it was possible on this instrument to record the radio stars with or without the background according to the arrangement of the receiving system.

Michelson's classical experiment on the measurement of diameters has been repeated many times for the radio sun and for

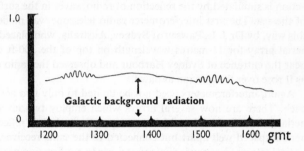

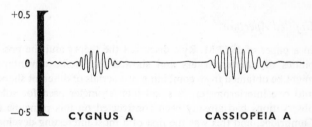

46. Interferometer recordings of two radio stars. The top record was made with a 'total power' recording, and shows radiation from the Milky Way; the lower recording was made with a receiver which records only the radio stars

radio stars. Further, it has been possible to carry out his suggestion of measuring brightness distributions, and some of the results are shown in Figures 3 and 4. Here are the only measurements of the size of the radio sun at long wavelengths. No steerable paraboloid can achieve this resolution, as it would have to be over a thousand feet in diameter.

Variety in radio interferometers runs the whole gamut of variety possible in the single aerials placed at either end. Paraboloids, cylindrical paraboloids, arrays of dipoles, all are used according to the aperture and the wavelength of reception. One particular type of interferometer, however, uses only one aerial; by placing this on top of a high cliff overlooking the sea the interferometer action is simulated by the reflection of radio waves in the surface of the sea. The first interferometer radio telescope was made in this way, by Dr J. L. Pawsey of Sydney, Australia, who placed an aerial array for $1\frac{1}{2}$-metres wavelength on top of the 300-ft cliff near the entrance of Sydney Harbour and observed the radio sun as it rose over the horizon at dawn.

Again, interferometers need not be limited to only two aerials each. There are now several arrays which employ two lines of aerials, each of which has thirty-two separate paraboloid reflector aerials spaced well apart but connected to the same receiver. In optical terms this array is analogous more to a diffraction grating than to an interferometer.

Unfilled Apertures

In a paper of 1952 M. Ryle discussed the theory and the possibilities of interferometers and showed that some advantages might be obtained from combining two aerials of different shapes into one interferometer. A small interferometer used for solar observations had already been constructed on this principle in Cambridge, and this was the first of a most interesting development which has no parallel in optical telescopes. The idea is illustrated in Figure 47.

All radio astronomers are in need of larger collecting areas than can be made, and all are in need of larger resolving powers. The two do not exactly go together. Suppose the dimensions of A are sufficient for the required resolving power, say 10 minutes of arc, which would be very useful in radio star work. In fact, to gain the advantages of an interferometer, two such apertures might be wanted, as in diagram B. The interferometer shown in C has less collecting area, which is not always intolerable, but it has only a very low resolving power in the north-south direction. The inter-

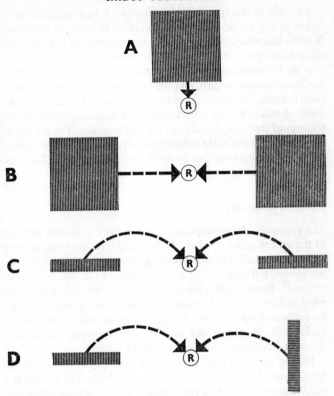

47. The development of the unfilled aperture: (A) single aperture – pencil beam; (B) two apertures – interferometer; (C) interferometer with poor north-south resolution; (D) crossed interferometer

ferometer in D with one aerial resolving in the east-west direction, and the other in the north-south direction, achieves the same resolution as the large pencil beam aerial but with a great saving in area. For long wavelengths, which is just where angular resolution is so hard to achieve, the loss of sensitivity does not greatly matter, as all celestial radio sources are stronger at long wavelengths.

An aerial of this type, in which only part is built while the resolution of the whole is obtained, is called an 'unfilled aperture'. B. Mills in Sydney, built the first large instrument of this type. His radio telescope, known as the 'Mills Cross' is shown in Plate 16. It is an interferometer, but the spacing between the two aerials has been reduced to zero, and the two arms are superimposed to form a cross. The advantage of the interferometer, in the improvement of contrast over a background, is retained, while various features of the background itself are still recorded. The essence of the Mills Cross lies in the achievement of a pencil beam resolution of about 50 minutes of arc at the long wavelength of 3·7 metres, or about 12 feet.

Aperture Synthesis

The economy of construction in the unfilled aperture, whether of the spaced aerial or of the Mills Cross type, does not entirely overcome the difficulties of obtaining high resolving power at long wavelengths. There is still a lot of aerial to build, and, more seriously, there is still a lot of aerial to join together with transmission lines. Although the east-west arm can for most purposes be connected up once and for all, the north-south arm must be variable in its connexions to allow for swinging the beam to different elevations. This is very hard to achieve.

Having made an unfilled aperture, the designer may well ask how much of an aperture must in fact be built. The answer is a surprising one: just two small sections only. But as Michelson said for his one-dimensional interferometer, the spacings between these two must be changed both in size and direction, with a full series of observations made at each position. Figure 48 shows how this can be understood and used. The principle is called 'aperture synthesis', since a full-size aperture is obtained by adding up a series of small apertures.

In the figure, the synthesis of a single large aperture is shown. Dividing the aperture up into units of the size of the small moveable aerials, each possible contribution of angle and distance, such as AB, CD, etc., must be separately explored, moving an aerial between each observation and the next. It would seem that an

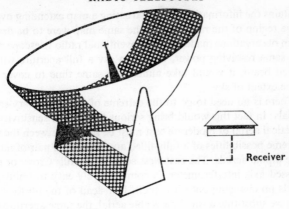

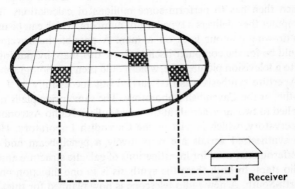

48. Aperture synthesis. A single large paraboloid may be simulated by two smaller aerials which can be placed at various distances apart in the same sized aperture

impossibly long time would be taken for each sweep of the sky, but this is not so. Admittedly each series of observations must be completed before any part of a map can be drawn, but each series contains the information for constructing a map extending over a large region of the radio sky. If the same map were to be drawn from observations made with a conventional radio telescope with the same resolving power, that is to say a full aperture with a pencil beam, it would take almost the same time to cover the same extent of sky.

There is no need to go to the extreme of using two very small aerials; in fact this would bring serious troubles of sensitivity. A practical aerial of moderate cost must be sought between the two extreme possibilities of a fully-filled aperture and a pair of moveable dipole aerials. The east-west aerial of a Mills Cross, or of a crossed axis interferometer, is comparatively easy to build and needs no changing once it is built. If instead of the north-south arm we substitute a small moveable aerial, the same aperture can be 'synthesized' by moving this aerial along the north-south line. The actual construction of a map of the sky by this synthesis technique is a complicated matter. All the observations here are recorded on punched tape and fed into an electronic computer, which then has to perform some millions of calculations. The computer then delivers a typed list of numbers, which can be used for drawing contour lines on a map. A possible improvement would be for the computer itself to draw this map, by putting it on to a television picture tube, which could then be photographed.

Aperture synthesis was first carried out successfully by J. H. Blythe, at the Cavendish Laboratory. The same principle is now applied to two large aerials at the new Mullard Radio Astronomy Observatory, which is part of the Cavendish Laboratory. Here the synthesized aerials are respectively a pencil-beam and an interferometer, used for investigations of galactic structure and of radio stars. In both these the synthesis is in one direction only, North-South. A new radio telescope is now planned for this observatory, using as its elements three paraboloids only 60 ft in diameter. Again by using the earth's rotation, and by tracking one area of sky through the day, a two-dimensional synthesis of an aperture close to one mile in diameter will be achieved.

Summary of Techniques

Radio telescopes today exhibit such a wide variety that it is hard to see the principles which unite them. A brief recapitulation of these various principles may be of value in understanding the various instruments described in Chapter 20.

Firstly, the requirement of sensitivity dictates a large collecting area, measured sometimes in acres. The larger the area, the larger the sensitivity. Secondly, angular resolving power dictates the total linear extension of aerials, whether or not the whole aperture is filled with aerials.

Resolving power is of two kinds, one which determines the ability to distinguish between adjacent individual radio stars, and the other the ability to measure accurately the position and diameter of a radio star which has been clearly distinguished from its neighbours. Positions and diameters are best measured with the use of an interferometer aerial system, and the resolving power in this sense is determined by the separation between the aerials rather than by their individual size.

Unfilled apertures therefore, in one way or another, achieve a higher resolving power than their area alone would suggest. The amount of aerial structure that can be 'left out' of an unfilled aperture is determined by the available sensitivity of the receiver, since a very sensitive receiver can make the most of the signals that are received even from a small area of actual aerial. Since the longer wavelength radiations give larger signals it is at these wavelengths that unfilled aperture aerials are most useful.

Aperture synthesis too is most useful at longer wavelengths, for it also requires a good receiver sensitivity. It can be applied to almost any kind of radio telescope, interferometer or pencil-beam, but in practice it is likely to be used in conjunction with an unfilled aperture. The most powerful radio telescope in the world, that operating on a wavelength of 1·7 metres at Cambridge, uses the principles of an interferometer, an unfilled aperture, and aperture synthesis all together, which makes it rather a complicated instrument. Simplicity is more to be expected at the shorter wavelengths, where the most useful way of using a collecting area is to concentrate it into a single parabolic reflector.

CHAPTER 19

Receivers

IN a radio telescope the part played by the radio receiver is similar to that of the photographic plate at the focusing point of an optical telescope. It is the point at which electromagnetic waves received over a large collecting area and focused to a point are converted into some recordable form. Descriptions of optical telescopes always refer to the size of the lenses or reflectors and to the arrangements for focusing the light. Not much mention is made of the photographic plate, and indeed the fact that new developments in recording involve replacing the photographic plate by an electronic image-converter seems to be of interest only to the astronomers using the telescopes. In the same way the receiving apparatus in a radio telescope, however novel, is hardly likely to be mentioned when a new radio telescope is described. The aerial to which it is attached will always steal the picture.

Nevertheless the receiving side of radio astronomy is of such importance that it cannot be overlooked; and furthermore there are some recent new developments in receiver techniques which will have as great an effect on radio astronomy as the image converter will have on optical astronomy.

The one outstanding requirement of a radio receiver used as part of a radio telescope is that it should be sensitive, and the history of these receivers is one of greater and greater emphasis on sensitivity. They are required to amplify and record the very small voltages that the aerial feeds into them, without distorting it by fluctuations in the receiver itself. From the modified wartime radar receivers used in the early days of radio astronomy there has been a steady progress in sensitivity and stability, and now the recent inventions of several different types of amplifier make possible an almost incredibly sensitive apparatus.

As the receiver's main task is to take a very small voltage and present it to a mechanical recorder as a larger one, the amplifying part of the set will be of great importance. Any amplifier tends to introduce its own unwanted signals into a receiver, whether it is a valve amplifier, a transistor amplifier, parametric amplifier, or what you will; the signals generated in any of these amplifiers have unfortunately many of the characteristics of the wanted signals. Both the wanted and the unwanted signals, compounded of a random assortment of frequencies, are termed 'noise'. Tuning in to cosmic noise on a receiver with loudspeaker output produces very much the same hissing sound as can be heard from an amplifier with no output at all, generated in the valves themselves. Distinguishing between receiver noise and cosmic noise is thus one of the fundamental problems of a radio telescope receiver.

Amplifiers with a Low Noise Level

Cosmic radio noise can be specified as a temperature, and so can receiver noise. Figure 49 shows the 'noise temperature' of a good receiver, using the best possible components, plotted against

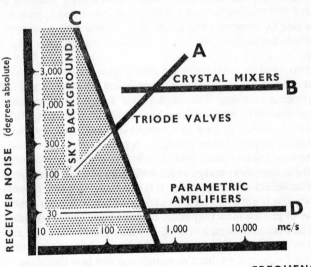

49. The variation of receiver noise with frequency
for different kinds of amplifier

working frequency. The scales of this graph are plotted logarithmically, which gives a more even emphasis to the range of frequencies used in radio astronomy. Graph A shows the noise generated in valve amplifiers. For example, at a frequency of 300 Mc/s (wavelength of one metre), a good triode valve generates only 300° K of noise, but at higher frequencies the situation becomes rapidly worse. At frequencies above 1,000 Mc/s it is better to use a crystal detector than a valve, and the line B shows the results from good crystals.

The sky background itself adds a component to this noise temperature, of an amount which falls rapidly with frequency (Graph C), and at low frequencies, say less than 200 Mc/s; this is the main source of noise when a particular radio star is being examined against this background. No improvement in sensitivity can be made here by using better amplifiers. In fact 'the sky's the limit.' But at high frequencies the receiver is the limiting factor, and it is here that tremendous advances are being made. It is hoped that receiver noise at any frequency may be held down below line D, corresponding to 30° K only, and giving improvements in sensitivity of over ten times that of conventional amplifiers.

Two separate amplifiers have been developed simultaneously that can provide this amazing improvement: the Maser and the parametric amplifier. The word Maser stands for Microwave Amplification by the Stimulated Emission of Radiation. It is fully understandable only by a rather detailed quantum theory, but a rough explanation can be attempted. A piece of crystalline material (a ruby has been used) held at a low temperature in a magnetic field can store away energy which it will emit as a radio frequency oscillation either strongly, when it is stimulated to do so, or more slowly if it is not stimulated. The stimulation comes from a radio wave of just the same frequency, so that a wave can be amplified by the fresh oscillation it sets off. The energy is stored in the crystal by another oscillator of a more conventional type and with a higher frequency, so that this energy pumped into the Maser at one frequency emerges as an amplified signal at another.

A Maser, then, is a crystal mounted in a waveguide and energized by an oscillator, so that radio waves from an aerial are amplified and fed into a normal receiver. The practical difficulties at present are great: the Maser must be immersed in liquid helium, and it must be supplied with a precisely stabilized magnetic field and a precise amount of power from the 'pumping' oscillator. Nevertheless, it works.

The parametric amplifier is not a quantum device, nor does it need to operate at very low temperatures. The word 'parametric' implies that amplification is achieved by a change in the parameters of a circuit. Lord Rayleigh described a parametric amplification of a mechanical oscillation as long ago as 1883, and in fact the achievement of mechanical amplification dates much further back, to the unknown time when a child first found out how to 'work' himself up on a swing, by shifting his weight to produce a cyclic change of moment of inertia. The energy which is transferred to the swinging motion comes from this cyclic change of the main parameter of the system. Electrically, the parameter which is changed is usually the capacity of a condenser, and the change is induced by an oscillator, called a 'pump'. Energy from the pump goes into amplifying a radio signal, just as in an ordinary amplifier a battery or power pack supplies energy to an amplifying valve or transistor.

Parametric amplifiers already exist in several forms suitable for high frequency amplification, and all of these resemble the Maser in this conversion of pump energy into amplification. Some also resemble the Maser in their use of a 'crystal' as the point where the energy is transferred. But the crystals are of the catswhisker diode type, not the large pure crystals used in Masers: nor are low temperatures required for parametric amplifiers. It is likely that these amplifiers will turn out to be nearly as easy to make and to use as an ordinary triode amplifier; certainly they will be about ten times as good.

Special Types of Receivers

There are large differences in detail between radio astronomy receivers for different purposes, but they must all be concerned with the measurement of a small noise signal in the presence of a large unwanted noise signal. For a pencil beam survey of the sky, all that can be done is to measure the total sky noise, rejecting only the receiver noise. This is called a 'total power' technique. An interferometer recognizes only the radio waves from small sources, and rejects the sky background. Receivers for interferometers use the technique of 'phase-switching', which produces the improvements of Figure 46. A receiver for the hydrogen line at 1420 Mc/s must isolate a very narrow band of frequencies only, comparing the strength with that of adjacent bands. All these procedures involve special techniques with which we need not concern ourselves here, but the point should be made that all involve the measurement of very small powers indeed, of the same nature as 'receiver noise', and that all will benefit from the introduction of new amplifiers to the extent of the improvement shown in Figure 49.

Improvement of performance of this order offers the possibility of quite new discoveries. Looking ahead, and in the most obvious direction, one can foresee the detection of several more of the planets and possibly the achievement of radio echoes from Venus. Many more ionized hydrogen clouds in the galactic plane, and many planetary nebulae will come within the range of detection. One most valuable result will be the improvement in the hydrogen spectral line survey at 21 cm., which will give more details of the spiral structure of our own galaxy and of several other galaxies as well.

The effect on the most exciting problem in radio astronomy, the search for knowledge of the origin of the universe, is harder to predict. Here the most penetrating observations are being made at lower frequencies, and reductions of receiver noise will be of no use unless working frequencies are raised to a point where the background noise is of less importance. This raises some very difficult problems of aerial construction.

Achievements in Sensitivity

Broadcast transmitters commonly attain powers of ten or a hundred kilowatts, but such a small fraction of this is picked up by a normal receiver that its sensitivity has to reach down to the level of 10^{-12} watts, or one billionth of a watt. This is nothing to the radio astronomer. He takes a receiver as sensitive as he can find, which may produce a 'noise' level of only 10^{-14} watts, and he then proceeds to look for signals less than one thousandth of this level. This is achieved by a process of averaging, by which the average output of the receiver over several seconds of time is measured. The longer the time, the more accurate the average. Also for a 'noise' signal, the wider the frequency response of a receiver the more accurate is the measured average, and hence the greater becomes the sensitivity. Three ingredients go into the recipe for great sensitivity: a 'low noise' amplifier, a wide bandwidth, and a long averaging time.

The new amplifiers are not yet widely used, although their noise performances are certain to give substantial improvements in sensitivity. The second factor, a wide bandwidth, has indeed been used, in a receiver built for the Greenbank Observatory. Normal triode amplifiers usually have a bandwidth of less than 10 Mc/s; this receiver uses a 'Travelling Wave Tube' or T.W.T. amplifier with a bandwidth of 1,000 Mc/s. (Shortwave radio communication links now quite commonly use T.W.T. amplifiers because of their wide bandwidth. In such an amplifier, electrons are formed into a narrow beam guided down several inches of tube; oscillations induced in one end of the beam grow as they travel along, and emerge many times amplified.)

The Greenbank receiver is sensitive to about one hundredth of a degree change of affective temperature; a direct measurement of this sensitivity can actually be made by using it to measure the temperature of a water bath surrounding a dummy aerial. A few drops of hot water in a large cold bath can make a detectable rise in temperature. On a small radio telescope aerial it has been used to detect thermal radio waves from planets and from planetary nebulae; the smallest detected signal, from the planet Saturn, gave an aerial temperature of one twenty-fifth of a degree. On the Greenbank radio telescope this receiver should be able to detect the thermal radio waves from a Sputnik 200 miles above the earth, provided that it was warmed to any temperature above freezing point.

Longer wavelength radio telescopes can also claim records for sensitivity. Collecting radio waves from an area of two acres, the

Cambridge radio interferometer can detect power fluxes below one unit, where the unit is 10^{-26} watts per square meter per unit bandwidth. If the same receiver, using the same bandwidth, were able to collect radiation of this intensity not from two acres, but from the whole of our planet, the total power would still only be one millionth of a watt. A transmitter on the surface of the moon giving a power of only one hundredth of a watt could give this minimum detectable signal. But such are the vastnesses of space that on the nearest star the most powerful transmitter yet constructed would be over a million times too feeble to make itself heard in our solar system.

Amateur Radio Astronomy

Grote Reber became a radio astronomer when he found that exploration of this world by amateur radio had been completed. As he put it: 'My interest in radio astronomy began after reading the original articles by Karl Jansky. For some years previous I had been an ardent radio amateur and considerable of a DX addict, holding the call sign W9GFZ. After contacting over sixty countries and making W.A.C. (worked all continents), there did not appear to be any more worlds to conquer.'

Any radio amateur who today feels the urge to explore further than his own planet need not step so far into the unknown as did Reber when he built his backyard radio telescope in 1937. There is now a special section of the British Astronomical Association which coordinates the work of amateur radio astronomers; during the hectic days which followed the launching of Sputnik I the organizer of this amateur section, J. Heywood of the Norwood Technical College, collected information from a network of radio observers covering the whole country. Norwood now has a working radio telescope that can be transported anywhere and set up as a demonstration, say in a school playground or as part of a scientific exhibition. The value of a live demonstration of solar radio waves in the teaching of astronomy in schools is obvious. How much effort does it cost to produce such a worthwhile radio telescope?

I think that an amateur must rest content with the detection at

BROADSIDE AERIALS

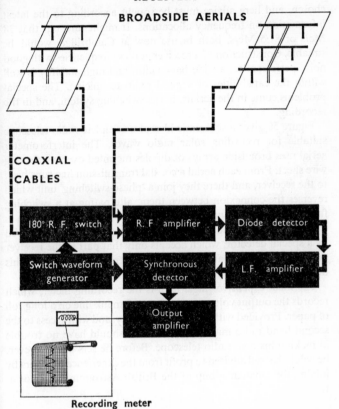

Recording meter

50. A simple radio telescope, suitable for recording
radio waves from the sun

a fairly long wavelength of the strongest of the celestial radio
sources, that is the sun, and the two radio stars Cygnus A and
Cassiopeia A. He should attempt to record their signals as clearly
and as accurately as possible. The variability of the solar radio
waves and the scintillation of the radio stars both make most
interesting studies; systematic work on either may prove to have
scientific value. A frequency clear from interference must be

chosen, and here advice must be sought according to the latest information on frequency allocations. It might turn out that 38 Mc/s or 81·5 Mc/s, both in use now at Cambridge, would be suitable. Construction of a receiver at these frequencies with good noise performance, a wide bandwidth, and high stability is well within the capabilities of a good radio technician. The special problems come in the aerials, in the switching system, and in the recording.

Figure 50 gives a schematic idea of a complete radio telescope suitable for recording solar radio waves. The interferometer aerial uses broadside arrays of dipoles mounted over a reflecting wire sheet. From each aerial a coaxial transmission line runs back to the receiver, and there they join a 'phase-switching' unit which reverses the connexion between them, alternating at a switching frequency of some hundreds of cycles per second. The switch is operated by crystal diodes. Then comes the receiver itself, followed by a special detector, which accepts only that part of the receiver output which alternates at the switch frequency. Finally this detector actuates via another amplifier a recording meter.

The most expensive single item is the recording meter, which records the output voltage in the form of an ink line on a long roll of paper. Provided with this, with ingenuity, and with access to the second-hand radio market, the amateur should have no trouble in making his own radio telescope. Before he sets out, however, he would be well advised to profit from the experience of others by joining the amateur group of the British Astronomical Association.

CHAPTER 20

The World's Radio-Astronomical Observatories

EVERY three years the International Astronomical Union meets in General Assembly, and astronomers from all over the world join in discussions of every aspect of astronomy, from time-keeping to telescope making, and from the insides of stars to the outer parts of the universe. During the last two Assemblies, in which the main meetings have been held at Dublin and at Moscow, the pressure of meetings on radio astronomy has been so great that separate symposia were held for this subject alone. These meetings were held in Manchester (1955) and in Paris (1958), and they each lasted a week. Only a few representatives of each radio observatory were there, but there were nevertheless over two hundred at the Paris meetings. Twelve years earlier there were only about a dozen radio astronomers in the world, and twelve years before that only one. Where have they come from, where do they work, and what do they all do?

Astronomical research has traditionally been an individual enterprise, fostered by Universities and receiving little assistance from the State. It is true that the Royal Greenwich Observatory was founded in 1675 by Charles II for the specific purpose of aiding navigation at sea, and it is true that this famous Observatory, now removed to Herstmonceux, is still run by the Admiralty. But Flamsteed, the first Astronomer Royal, himself had to spend large sums of his own money in equipping the Observatory, and State support through the Admiralty is still on no lavish scale.* Of the telescopes at Herstmonceux half date back to last century, and no telescope in the whole country has an aperture greater than 36 in. English Universities have fared no better than Herstmonceux, particularly if one makes a comparison with the times of greatness brought to this country by Herschel and to Ireland by Lord Rosse, who constructed and successfully used a 72-in.

* The Admiralty is now providing funds for the construction of the 98-in. Isaac Newton telescope at Herstmonceux.

reflector telescope in 1845. Again a contrast may be made with the endowment of the great telescopes in America, culminating with the $6,000,000 contributed by the Rockefeller Foundation to the construction of the 200-in. telescope of Mt Palomar.

Radio astronomy is developing in an age of extraordinarily rapid scientific progress. Since the war it has covered many of the phases of development which took ten times as long for optical astronomy. Starting with individual efforts, in which we ought properly to include those of Edison and Lodge, and other unsuccessful attempts to detect solar radio waves, we find the first radio astronomy pursued with great vigour but in isolation by Jansky and by Reber. It was only after the war that the stimulation of Hey's work in the Army Operational Research Group led to the beginnings of three established radio observatories which remain today as three of the largest in the world. Two, at Cambridge (the Mullard Observatory) and Manchester (Jodrell Bank), are University Observatories. The third, in Sydney, is run by the Commonwealth Scientific and Industrial Research Organization as part of its Radiophysics Laboratory. The Sydney radio astronomers are therefore Civil Servants, just as they would be if they were in the Royal Greenwich Observatory, although in geographical location and in academic affinities they are very close to University research.

On the Continent of Europe it has been the Observatories of Meudon, in Paris, and of Leiden, that have contributed most to radio astronomy. Here radio has been regarded very properly as an extension of the conventional techniques long employed there, and here again radio astronomy becomes part of an essentially university activity. Under the direction of a permanent staff, research students learn the techniques and discipline of a new subject and are given opportunities for individual research. Many leave astronomy after this training and after attaining their Doctor's degree, but with the rapid growth of radio astronomy many go to the new radio observatories which are beginning all over the world.

Continuing on the same line of university development come many universities in the U.S.A., notably Harvard, where the hydrogen line was first detected. In the U.S.S.R. the organization of astronomy is rather different, with observatories and research institutes less directly connected with universities. Direct and generous State support is the rule, without any apparent loss of autonomy or vitality in the observatories. Indeed without large State funds there would be no astronomy of any kind in Russia today, for all their major observatories including the famous Pulkova near Leningrad were totally destroyed during the last war.

Intense national competition has now developed in radio astronomy, with the emergence of Soviet science and with the reawakening of American radio astronomy. There is no doubt of the national prestige that accrues from such a spectacular instrument as the 250-ft reflector at Jodrell Bank, and it must stand to the credit of any government when it helps to finance any such scientific project. National prestige has recently, however, become an uncomfortably important factor in the distribution of scientific money. There is an international race in progress to explore space with satellites and moon probes, and one hardly needs quote the grand Russian successes to illustrate the prestige value of spectacular scientific ventures. Radio astronomy is apparently benefiting from this race, since it plays an important part in satellite tracking, and we may anticipate, with some uneasiness, seeing the next generation of radio telescopes designed with one eye on their usefulness for slightly less than pure astronomy, so that a sideline activity may produce finance for the real job in hand. Perhaps one should not usually look a gift horse in the mouth, but scientists have found that they must develop a keen sensitivity to any suggestion that would divide their attention between essentials and non-essentials.

Fortunately, as will clearly be seen in the list of instruments at the various observatories, no such baleful influence is discernable so far. Competition there must indeed be, and it is a most stimulating competition in which every advance is seized on and built upon by others as soon as results are published. Even close duplication of instruments is not harmful at the present stage, since a definite confirmation of previous new results is a valuable and most necessary part of any new science.

The radio observatories, then, are of the same mixture as the optical observatories. A few are run as an amateur's hobby.

Many are government institutions working under more or less direct departmental control: the majority are university observatories or are part of some other independent institution, and in both their work combines the training of research students with the discipline of pure astronomy. There is a corresponding variety of radio astronomers, some of whom spend their whole lives on research, while some combine varying proportions of teaching or university administration. There is also now a steady flow out from radio astronomy of scientists trained in the hard school of research, who have spent three or four years learning how to be inquisitive, objective, determined, and interested, and how to present their findings to the world as published scientific papers.

A List of Radio Observatories

The following list of observatories is not intended to be exhaustive and complete. It includes the major radio observatories of each country and shows how each has made and is now making its own special contributions to astronomy. Emphasis on some particular discoveries, or on particular instruments, may often mean only that they have particularly impressed or interested the author.

As he glances through this list, each reader will be looking for some aspect of the observatories which particularly interests him, whether it be their history, their organization, or perhaps only the relative dimensions of their various radio telescopes. Whatever this special interest he should bear in mind primarily the differentiation in objectives that is now so evident in the various observatories. There are small observatories, for example, whose object is a simple but effective 'solar patrol', a continuous watch on the sun's radio emission, possibly only at one radio frequency. Research of this limited nature is well suited to smaller universities, where little effort can be spared for post-graduate training, but where a critical approach to experimental work and to the handling of observational results can only effectively be taught by practice.

There are also Government establishments, such as the Naval Research Laboratory in Washington, and the Radiophysics

Laboratory in Sydney, where national resources are used to ensure on the one hand the continuance of a healthy tradition of scientific research, and on the other a reserve of scientific manpower. In these the government has clearly recognized the value of encouraging individual scientific enterprise, and many diverse lines of research may be concentrated in one very active establishment.

Again, old established observatories are now providing a foundation for radio observatories, and these are likely to follow in some way the traditions of the optical work; as for instance Leiden Observatory has guided Dutch radio astronomy primarily towards the determination of galactic structure by 21-cm. hydrogen line observations. All these influences are reflected in the size of the observatories, in the kind of work they undertake, and more particularly in the radio telescopes they construct.

The list which follows is in alphabetical order of countries, and owes much to a recent list of radio observatories published by the International Astronomical Union.

AUSTRALIA

The Radiophysics Laboratory, Sydney

This laboratory is part of the Commonwealth Scientific and Industrial Research Organization. During the war it was a centre for radar research. Immediately at the end of the war, work was begun there on solar radio waves under Dr J. L. Pawsey, who is now the Director. With a record of rapid and most enterprising development this laboratory now stands as one of the longest established and most distinguished of the world's radio observatories. To record all its outstanding contributions would be to repeat much of this book, since they cover most fields of interest.

Pawsey's solar work was achieved with the cliff interferometer, using a single aerial mounted on top of the 300-ft cliff at Dover Heights, just south of the entrance to Sydney Harbour. It was here also that John Bolton made the first interferometer observations of a radio star, and with the help of another cliff interferometer mounted in New Zealand found the first positions of several of these then quite unidentified objects. The first identifications are also to be credited to Bolton, who suggested that the Crab Nebula and the nebula NGC 5128 in Centaurus were two of the discrete sources which he had found.

Solar radio waves are now studied at Sydney with two most interesting instruments, one to study the details of the various types of metre-wave burst emission from the disturbed sun, and the other to construct a complete picture of the sun's surface as seen by decimetre radio waves.

The bursts of emission from flares and sunspots have a complicated structure, varying rapidly with time and at any one time containing a frequency spectrum which may extend over a range of anything from one to several hundred megacycles. Recordings on a fixed frequency are totally inadequate for their understanding, but the radio spectrograph first used at Sydney by J. P. Wild sweeps the frequency of a receiver rapidly through a wide range and displays the whole spectrum on film several times every second. The complete picture of the structure of bursts obtained by Wild's radio-spectrograph has done far more than a mere classification of different types of bursts: it gave the first demonstration of the rapidly moving disturbances which travel out through the solar corona at speeds up to a tenth that of light.

The second solar instrument is called a radio-heliograph, which indicates that it is used for delineating a map of the sun's surface at a fixed radio wavelength. The resolution is 3′ arc, compared with the 30′ diameter of the sun, and the narrow beam is produced by an interferometer array of sixty-four paraboloidal reflectors in two perpendicular lines. 'Radio heliograph' is a long name for this, and it is usually known instead as the 'Chris-cross', after its inventor W. H. Christiansen.

High angular resolution is also needed for radio star surveys, and B. Y. Mills' invention of the cross aerial has contributed greatly to this. His aerial for 3·7 metres wavelength is in the same way called the 'Mills Cross'. It is this aerial that has provided much of the fuel for the spirited controversy about the nature of radio stars and their relation to cosmology.

Sydney is also the centre of Southern Hemisphere observations of the 21-cm. hydrogen line, and is working in collaboration with Leiden Observatory on the mapping of the spiral arm structure of the Galaxy. A larger paraboloid aerial is needed for this, and with the help of a grant of money from the Carnegie Institution a 210-ft paraboloid has just been built in Australia. This new instrument will help to maintain the high standing of this observatory, which is indeed the only large radio observatory in the Southern Hemisphere.

BELGIUM

A radio astronomy laboratory is now attached to the Royal Observatory in Belgium. The aerials are at Humain-Rochefort, where solar work is carried on with various interferometers and paraboloids.

CANADA

Distinguished work has been done at the National Research Council in Ottawa by D. W. R. McKinley and P. M. Millman, who solved many of the problems of meteor radar echoes, and by A. E. Covington, whose measurements of 10-cm. solar radio waves present an unbroken sequence over a complete sunspot cycle.

A new radio observatory is now being built in Western Canada, at Penticton in the Rocky Mountains. This site, with great natural beauty and with a very low level of interference, combined with the resources of the Dominion Observatory, should prove most attractive.

ENGLAND

The three main radio observatories in England are at Cambridge, Jodrell Bank, and Malvern.

Cambridge

The Cavendish Laboratory has a long tradition of radio research, under the leadership of J. A. Ratcliffe. Immediately after the war he encouraged M. Ryle, now Professor Ryle, to work on solar radio waves, and a new research group began to grow. From the early work on metre wavelengths, the techniques of interferometry were evolved and used to measure the distribution of radio brightness across the sun. In 1948 the first radio star measurements were made, and a succession of radio star interferometers of great sensitivity and resolving power have become the centre of Cambridge radio astronomy. These interferometers provided the first really accurate positions of radio stars, and the first measurement of their angular diameters. It was from these measurements that the radio stars Cygnus A and Cassiopeia A were identified. Cambridge can also claim, among other discoveries, the discovery of the origin of radio scintillation, the first measurements of a radio occultation by the solar corona and of occultation by the moon, the discovery of the galactic halo, and the first reported orbit of Sputnik I. Science does not consist merely of discoveries, and these records must give place to a brief account of the new Mullard Radio Observatory now in operation at Cambridge, where two of the world's largest radio telescopes are being used to explore our galaxy and, beyond that, the furthermost reaches of the universe. (The Mullard Radio Observatory is named after the large benefaction received by Cambridge University from Mullard Ltd.)

The galactic radio telescope is designed to produce a 1° beam at a wavelength of 8 metres; no detailed map of the galactic radio emission at such a long wavelength is available as yet, although it is of great importance in the theory of galactic structure. It is impossible to make a full aperture to achieve this, as about sixty acres of aerial would be required; consequently the principle of aperture synthesis is used. One part of the aerial is 3,300 feet long, extended along an east-west line, with a collecting area of two acres, and the other part is a movable aerial which is used at distances up to 1,800 feet from the fixed line (Plate 15B).

Interferometers for radio stars are often complicated enough to understand, but the new Mullard radio star interferometer is the most difficult of all. The two halves are extended in different directions, one east-west and the other north-south, and the two halves are separated by 2,600 feet. The east-west half is fixed, and is a cylindrical paraboloid 1,650 feet by 60 feet, an area of two acres. The north-south half is an area 1,000 feet by 200 feet, but it is made by aperture synthesis. A moving aerial 60 feet by 200 feet runs on a railway track, so that the whole area may be covered in about three weeks' observations (Plates 14B, 15A). This is the most sensitive radio star instrument so far constructed; its recent successful observations have cleared away much of the uncertainty surrounding the cosmological significance of distant radio stars. It is also a versatile instrument: the large fixed aerial is useful in its own right as the finest pencil beam instrument available for scanning the sky at metre wavelengths, and the two aerials together may be used as an interferometer for finding extremely accurate positions for radio stars. Over sixty positions accurate to one minute of arc in both coordinates have already been obtained; with this accuracy identifications with visible objects can be attempted with a better hope of success.

Jodrell Bank

This world-famous observatory has grown from the meteor radar experiments conducted in 1947 by its director, Prof. A. C. B. Lovell, in a trailer on the site of the present buildings. The 250-ft paraboloid is well known and needs no description here. Its uses are many and various, including the tracking of satellites and lunar probes, the advantage over other instruments being not so much its sensitivity (the collecting area is about one acre) as its flexibility in working frequency and the full 'steerability' in azimuth and elevation.

The satellite-tracking achievements of the 250-ft paraboloid have rather overshadowed the more academic work which it is now achieving. We must also remember that most productive era in the history of Jodrell Bank around 1950, when so much of meteor astronomy and meteor physics came from there. At that time also, radio star work was carried on very productively with a fixed paraboloid, 220 feet in diameter, which was used to explore the sky near the zenith. For the measurement of radio star diameters, a new type of interferometer was devised by R. Hanbury Brown and R. Q. Twiss, which could be used with baselines of many miles. They have since then applied a similar technique to visible stars, and Hanbury Brown has achieved the notable feat of measuring the diameter of Sirius, a star too small for Michelson's original interferometer technique.

Moon echoes were obtained at Jodrell Bank in 1954, and the most rewarding studies of the fading of echoes, which give information on the surface of the moon and on the Faraday rotation of the ionosphere, were originated there.

Malvern

Dr J. S. Hey's pioneer work in British radio astronomy was done in a research group attached to the army. He now runs part of the Physics division of the Royal Radar Establishment at Malvern. It is pleasant to record that he is now building up a considerable radio observatory there, with a versatile interferometer using two 85-ft paraboloid 'dishes', mounted on railway tracks. This will be used for accurate positional work on radio stars, at wavelengths down to 10 cm. At Malvern there is also a 45-ft paraboloid, which has been used for moon echoes, and for a search for deuterium line radiation from the Galaxy.

FRANCE

The two radio observatories in France are based on Institutions in Paris, and are related to two famous optical observatories, those of Meudon near Paris and of Haute-Provence in the south of France. At Saint-Michel, where the new Observatory of Haute-Provence is to be found in some of the loveliest of the French countryside, M. Laffineur is constructing a large radio star interferometer. At Nançay, some ninety miles south of Paris, an entirely new observatory is now operating most successfully, under the leadership of Dr J. F. Denisse.

At Nançay, the most powerful and the most spectacular instrument is a large 32-element interferometer. This occupies a strip of land a mile long, carved out of the forest, and uses thirty-two paraboloids similar to those used by Christiansen in Sydney. The wavelength, however, is two metres instead of 20 cm., so that the scale of the apparatus is ten times greater. This instrument is used for scanning the sun at a longer wavelength, where the variability of radio emission is much greater.

The French radio astronomers have so far been concerned mainly with solar studies, and with the most interesting and complicated relationships between various radio disturbances on the sun and various terrestrial effects such as magnetic disturbances and aurorae. They are now becoming interested in radio stars and in the 21-cm. line, and accordingly they are constructing a huge reflecting telescope of the Kraus type. So far a section 300 ft by 100 ft has been built.

GERMANY

Until a few years ago, Germany's chief contribution to radio astronomy was the network of 'Würzburg' radar stations established along the coast of Europe and abandoned after the war. Each station was equipped with a 27-ft parabolic aerial of excellent quality, and many of these aerials were later appropriated by the new radio observatories, both in Europe and America. Würzburg aerials were used at Cambridge, for example, in accurate positional measurements. Radio observatories have now started all over Germany, in Berlin-Aldersdorf, Bonn, Freiburg, Kiel, Potsdam, and Tübingen, and the country will clearly be taking an increasingly important part in radio astronomy. At Bonn, under Fr. Becker, an 80-ft paraboloid is being used for 21-cm. work, but apart from this the sun is the chief object of study. Here Prof. Kiepenheuer, of Freiburg, and Prof. Siedentopf, of Tübingen, bring to this new field a very wide experience of optical astronomy; radio astronomy which starts from only radio engineering is likely to be conducted with rather a naïve approach to the not inconsiderable body of optical knowledge of the sun.

JAPAN

There are five radio observatories in Japan, all working on solar radio waves. The two outstanding stations are at Nagoya and Tokyo.

Nagoya

Under the direction of H. Tanaka, the finest work on centi-
metric radio waves from the sun is carried on here. There is
another Christiansen-type interferometer, at 7-cm. wavelength,
giving resolution of $4\frac{1}{2}$ minutes of arc, and there are several other
interferometers and aerials for determining the polarization of
solar radio bursts.

Tokyo

Here a wider range of solar work under T. Hatanaka covers
radio emission on wavelengths from 4 metres to 3 cm. Polarization
and detailed structure of radio bursts can be investigated over
most of this band.

NETHERLANDS

Netherlands Foundation for Radio Astronomy

This government foundation draws together the resources of
the Observatories at Leiden, Utrecht, and Gröningen. It was at
Leiden that H. C. van de Hulst proposed the use of the 21-cm.
hydrogen line for studying Galactic structure, and it is this same
study, still carried on by Leiden Observatory, that forms the
main work of the joint radio observatory. The radio telescopes
are at a new observatory at Dwingeloo, chosen for its low noise
level. An 85-ft parabolic reflector is the main instrument, used
both for the 21-cm. line and for other galactic studies.

The great strength of the Netherlands Radio Observatory lies
in its direct association with an old established and most vigorous
optical observatory. The director, Prof. J. H. Oort, was an authority on Galactic structure long before the term radio astronomy
was coined. Combining the radio and optical pictures of the spiral
arms and of discrete sources like the Crab Nebula has been quite
naturally left to Leiden; but it is also true that the technical side
of the radio observations at 21 cm. has been better managed at
Leiden than anywhere else.

U.S.A.

Radio astronomy has returned to America in full force, after a decade during which the initiative lay unquestionably in England and Australia. There are now over twenty American radio observatories in operation, and it is increasingly difficult to keep track of all the paraboloidal reflectors in use.

U.S.A. Universities

Universities which are now engaged in radio astronomy include Alabama, Alaska, Cornell (New York), Florida, Harvard, Illinois, Michigan, Ohio, Stanford (California), and Yale. At many of these solar observations are the principal work, and receivers for the whole range of wavelengths, including several radio spectrographs, are now used in a continuous patrol of solar activity. Harvard has its own special radio observatory in Texas for this, and Michigan is constructing an 85-ft paraboloid primarily for solar spectroscopy. This latter radio telescope will complement the intensive solar work of the McMath Hulbert Observatory, which is part of the same University. It was at Harvard that the 21-cm. hydrogen line was first observed by H. I. Ewen, and the Agassiz Observatory there now carries on research into galactic structure with a 21-cm. receiver mounted on a 60-ft paraboloid.

Ohio State University is at Columbus, where Prof. Kraus who is an authority on aerial design now directs a programme of galactic and extra galactic research. A large aerial used there for mapping out the galactic emission on $1\frac{1}{2}$-metres wavelength uses Kraus's invention of the helical aerial; the array of ninety-six helices mounted on a large frame covered with wire netting looks very like the insides of a giant spring interior mattress.

Kraus has been a strong advocate of the large fixed parabolic reflector aerial, his own version comprising a curved, nearly vertical, reflecting wall which focuses to a point on the ground. The elevation of the beam will be changed by tilting another reflector, which has a plane surface, to reflect waves into the paraboloid. Both structures will be large; a start has been made with a reflector 200 ft long and 70 ft high.

Green Bank, West Virginia

It has now been clearly recognized in America that the largest and most expensive pieces of physical apparatus cannot be part of the normal equipment of a University. A new body, Associated Universities Incorporated, already provides for a group of universities first-class facilities for nuclear physics at Brookhaven; recently, under the leadership of L. V. Berkner, it has undertaken to provide similar facilities for radio-astronomical research for these universities and for any other visiting radio astronomers at Green Bank, Virginia. Green Bank is in quiet attractive country, in a valley between low mountains which shield it from man-made interference. A beautiful and precise parabolic radio telescope is being built there, which will be 140 feet in diameter but which will still operate on a wavelength of 3 cm. Its whole surface will therefore have to be correct to less than an eighth of an inch, whether it is looking straight upwards or horizontally towards the horizon. The guiding mechanism must be correct to a fraction of a minute of arc.

Such instruments are very expensive, and it is pleasing to see that universities, with help from the government, can effectively pool their resources of money and research talent to create such opportunities.

Pasadena (California)

J. G. Bolton, who was a pioneer of radio star interferometry in Sydney, now directs a radio observatory in the California Institute of Technology, which shares in the running of the Palomar 200-in. telescope. Two 90-ft paraboloids are being constructed on railway tracks, so that a variable spacing interferometer can be used for diameters and positions of radio stars at wavelengths down to 3 cm. (Plate 12).

Washington, D.T.M.

The Department of Terrestrial Magnetism of the Carnegie Institution of Washington is directed by M. A. Tuve, who was the first man to obtain a pulse echo from the ionosphere. The most remarkable achievement of the department in radio astronomy was the discovery of the bursts from Jupiter, found by chance in an experiment to measure fluxes of radio stars on long wavelengths. A new multichannel 21-cm. receiver is in use here, also a high resolution aerial for solar recording on 88-cm. wavelength.

Washington, N.R.L.

The Naval Research Laboratory has contributed more to radio astronomy than any other American observatory. The N.R.L. 50-ft paraboloid, mounted on the laboratory roof beside the River Potomac, was the first large reflector which worked on centimetre wavelengths. It is constructed out of solid aluminium panels, which were fitted together and turned on a vertical lathe to make an exact surface. Testing the beam, which at 1-cm. wavelength is only 3 minutes of arc across, has usually been achieved by focusing on to a small transmitter at the top of the Washington Monument, five miles away. With this reflector the first centimetre measurements of radio stars were made, and many H II regions were shown to be radio emitters.

N.R.L. has now a new 85-ft reflector, suitable for wavelengths down to 3 cm., at Maryland Point. With this, and with the 50-ft reflector, the new low-noise amplifiers will be used for short wavelength radio star studies. There is also a fixed paraboloid, 250 feet across, used for moon radar, at a neighbouring site.

Expeditions from N.R.L. have observed several solar eclipses with great success, using wavelengths of 3 cm. and 8 mm. to produce a picture of the lowest regions of the chromosphere.

U.S.S.R.

The resurgence of astronomy in the U.S.S.R. after the terrible destruction that came with the war has been accompanied by a rapid growth of radio astronomy. Technical backwardness is a thing of the past, and encouragement for all kinds of enterprise is evident. Most of the radio astronomy is centred on a research institute in Moscow, but the famous optical observatories are now joining in.

Burakan

At the Astrophysical Observatory in Armenia, a radio star interferometer is being built with cylindrical paraboloids like those of the Cavendish Laboratory, arranged as an unfilled aperture.

Moscow

The Lebedev Institute, which is a national institute for physical research, has two radio astronomical stations under the direction of V. Vitkevitch. At the Crimean station there are many radio telescopes, including the 100-ft concrete reflector used for polarization measurements, and interferometers for regular recordings of solar radio waves. A new station is now started at Sherpukhov, about fifty miles south of Moscow. Here larger radio telescopes are to be built. A 65-ft paraboloid reflector and a new cross aerial using cylindrical paraboloid reflectors several acres in area will both be used for radio star surveys.

Pulkova

This famous observatory near Leningrad now observes solar radiation at centimetre wavelengths with a new and most spectacular instrument (Plate 14A). An adjustable reflector surface covers an arc nearly 500 feet long, using individually adjustable solid plates 10 feet high by 5 feet wide. This arc reflects into a small aerial at its focus. The beam is directed towards the south, although the elevation can be changed through 80° by tilting the plates. In the east-west direction the beam is only 1 minute wide when 3-cm. wavelength is used.

During the most recent meeting of the International Astronomical Union the director of Pulkova, Prof. Khaikin, announced that the Observatory was planning a greatly enlarged version of this instrument, which would have a reflecting surface suitable for 21-cm. wavelength.

WHAT NEXT?

During the last decade the expansion of radio astronomy has been at a rapidly increasing pace. Both the number of observatories and the collecting area of large radio telescopes seem to be increasing by a geometrical progression. Undoubtedly the large instruments are necessary, and their contribution to astronomy is indeed already very considerable. One may, however, begin to doubt the usefulness of such a multiplicity of instruments as the preceding survey shows, and indeed it would have been more fortunate if more of these had been built in the Southern Hemisphere where the sky is not so well covered.

Will the construction of more new radio telescopes continue to advance astronomical knowledge in the same spectacular way as it has during this last decade?

Perhaps the most exciting field is that of the distant discrete radio stars, and it is in this field that we must regard the present generation of radio telescopes as only the experimental forerunners of some more powerful instruments. Design must follow on present results, but it is safe to predict that in some form or another a radio telescope with an area of at least ten acres, capable of working at wavelengths down to 50 cm., will be the logical next step. Can it be built? Whether it can or cannot, one vital question must be answered before any such serious undertaking can begin. This is the question of frequency planning.

Radio astronomy shares the radio spectrum with many other interests – communications, navigational aids, telemetering, radar, television. It is of no use to attempt serious radio astronomy unless a proper international agreement can be reached on the sharing of the spectrum among all these users. The agreement must be international, and it must be respected. Otherwise it will be as though an astronomer were to build a large telescope only to find that bright city lights were being installed just outside the telescope dome, or searchlights were being shone at the telescope from aircraft in the sky above. Clear recommendations on this frequency planning have been made by the International Astronomical Union, but it requires a willing and wholehearted support by the governments of many countries before it can take effect. One can only hope that the recent wide recognition of the value of the intellectual and scientific achievements of radio astronomy will bring this to pass, and make possible the proper development of this most exciting and satisfying endeavour.

APPENDIX

APPENDIX

Appendix

THE RADIO UNIVERSE
Some distances

Radio Observation	Distance in miles	Time of travel of light and radio waves
Unidentified radio stars	? over 5×10^{21}	? over 1000 million years
Hercules A – the most distant known radio nebula	5×10^{21}	800 million years
Cygnus A – the most powerful known radio nebula – a colliding galaxy.	3×10^{21}	550 million years
Virgo A – the 'blue jet' nebula – an elliptical galaxy	$2 \cdot 5 \times 10^{20}$	40 million years
The Andromeda Nebula – the nearest spiral galaxy	$1 \cdot 5 \times 10^{19}$	2 million years
The Magellanic Clouds – the nearest extralactic nebulae	$1 \cdot 5 \times 10^{18}$	200,000 years
The Galactic Centre – a radio 'hot spot'	2×10^{17}	30,000 years
Cassiopeia A – supernova remains in an adjacent spiral arm	6×10^{16}	10,000 years
The nearest visible star – no detectable radio waves	$2 \cdot 5 \times 10^{13}$	4 years
Jupiter – the radio planet	500 million	40 minutes
The Sun – the only known variable radio star	93 million	8 minutes
The Moon – seen by reflection, emission, and occultation of radio waves	220,000	$1\frac{1}{4}$ seconds
The Ionosphere – bending and distorting rays from the radio universe	200 miles	$\frac{1}{1000}$ second

Note. The distances quoted for the extragalactic objects depend on an assumed value for Hubble's Constant, which relates the red-shift of spectral lines to distance. Hubble's first value for this constant was 540 kilometres per second per kiloparsec, but recently it has been found that this value is very much too big. At present estimates vary between about 50 and 130; in the table a round number of 100 has been used throughout.

INDEX

Index

INDEX

Some other Pelicans
on science are described on
the following
pages

A History of Science and Technology
(2 Vols.)

E. J. DIJKSTERHUIS AND R. J. FORBES

A498, A499

The authors outline in these volumes the huge wealth of scientific knowledge and 'know-how' which Western civilization has piled up in the course of centuries and to which countless scientists and technologists have contributed.

So great was the quantity of material that they have deliberately excluded biology and medicine from the scope of their study, and concentrated on the sciences of inorganic matter. It is in essence a thrilling story – the tale of man's first diffident steps from cave and forest, of his gradually growing confidence, and of the undying urge to experiment which places him today at the threshold of other worlds.

VOLUME I

The first volume takes the story from the earliest signs of scientific thinking that archaeology can yield to (approximately) the close of the seventeenth century.

VOLUME II

The second volume outlines the main trends of science and technology during the eighteenth and nineteenth centuries, with relevant flashbacks to medieval and earlier practices. It emphasizes how much the technique of printing has accelerated the tempo of scientific progress, by placing new knowledge within the reach of all men.

AN INTRODUCTION TO THE PHYSICS OF

Mass length and time

NORMAN FEATHER

A532

Measurements of mass, length, and time are the fundamental measurements in physics. Professor Feather traces the history of the emergence of these three concepts, with their associated systems of measurement, from the earliest times. On this basis the whole subject of the mechanical properties of matter in bulk is developed. A unique feature of the book is its complete exclusion of the calculus, in any formal context. The author's express intention is to provide an understanding of principles and he devotes chapters to different kinds of motion, to force, mass, and inertia, to gravitation, energy of various sorts, elasticity, and surface tension. His biographical notes on the physicists he mentions add direct human interest to this explanation of 'what Physics is all about'. For essentially this book offers a friendly introduction to the science of Physics. 'What the author has in view . . . has been done admirably, in a way that will stimulate the general interest and broaden the mind of the youthful reader' – Professor Andrade in the *New Scientist*

The Evolution of Life

FRANK RHODES

A512

Life on Earth is not less than 2,500,000,000 years old. Of the last few thousand years – a tiny fraction of the whole – historians, mythologists, and archaeologists can give us an account which is more or less accurate. But the history of those vast expanses of time that preceded pre-history can only be studied, line by line, where it lies written in the rock.

Frank Rhodes recounts how palaeontologists have pieced together the story of the oldest organisms on earth and traced their slow evolution. He outlines the emergence and expansion of each of the great groups of living and extinct animals and plants, and discusses how they are related and what conditions, climatic and otherwise, they have encountered. The knowledge gained from this study helps us to an understanding of the basis of our own lives today.

Excellent illustrations and a glossary permit the general reader to appreciate this study of evolution as fully as the specialist.

Health and Hormones

A. STUART MASON

A487

What makes us tick? What makes us the sort of people we are? Why do some people appear genial and relaxed, others 'a bundle of nerves'? Is it true that fat people tend to be lazy? *Why* are some fat and others thin, anyhow?

In matters like these few people realize the importance of the endocrine system, for it does its job with secret efficiency. Yet the endocrine glands reach out, through their hormones, to influence every organ of the body and every aspect of living. They mould our bodies; protect us when we are ill; and, of course, govern every aspect of sex.

What is the thyroid really for? How do the adrenals control the life-giving mineral, salt? How does the pituitary dominate the other glands, and how does it link up with the brain? In answering these and other questions, *Health and Hormones* opens up for the reader new and fascinating aspects of human physiology.